TABLE OF CONTENTS

How the Modern Home Plumbing System Works

Where does the water come from; where does it go? Your home plumbing system is two separate systems, really--water supply and water disposal. Both are made up of several hundred feet of pipes and fittings that join them. Water in the water supply system is under pressure--some 50 pounds per square inch (psi). Thus, water supply pipes can be fairly small in diameter, yet still carry enough water. Water in the disposal, also called the drain-waste-vent (DWV) system, always flows by gravity. For this reason its pipes and fittings must be larger in diameter to carry the required flow without clogging or backing up. Both systems are designed to operate safely and quietly.

The systems, water supply and DWV, never are connected to each other. If contaminated water got into the drinking water, it could sicken or kill. Water from the water supply system flows into the drain-waste-vent system, never the other way around.

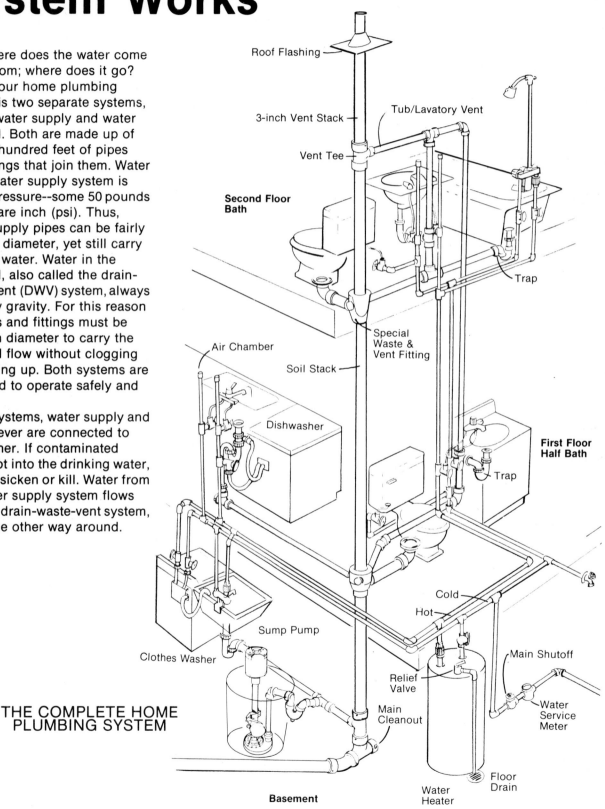

THE COMPLETE HOME PLUMBING SYSTEM

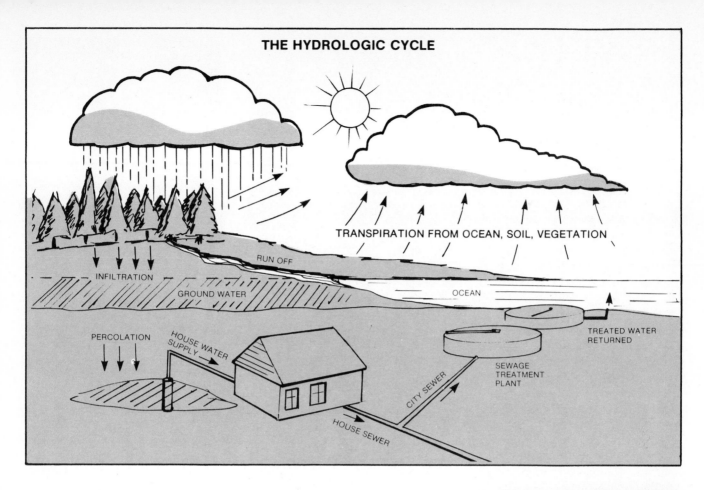

THE HYDROLOGIC CYCLE

TRANSPIRATION FROM OCEAN, SOIL, VEGETATION

RUN OFF

INFILTRATION

GROUND WATER

OCEAN

PERCOLATION

HOUSE WATER SUPPLY

TREATED WATER RETURNED

SEWAGE TREATMENT PLANT

CITY SEWER

HOUSE SEWER

WATER SUPPLY

Each adult in a family uses from 50 to 100 gallons of water a day. Each child under two needs 100 gallons a day. Your house water supply system either picks up its water from the city main underneath the street or else gets it from a well and pump in the yard. The system delivers water around the house to the various fixtures, appliances and outlets. The piping necessary to do this varies in size. Largest is about an inch in diameter, smallest ⅜ inch.

Where much water must flow, such as in the underground service entrance pipe that serves the whole house, the pipes are large. Where little water must flow, such as through a single fixture, the pipes are small.

The first place water goes is through a water meter, if you have one. After leaving the meter, water comes to a valve in the main house supply pipe. Called the main shutoff, this valve allows you to turn off all water to the whole house. Often this important valve is located at the low point of the water supply system and contains a separate drain opening. With the main valve off, you can drain the entire system. A draining valve is called a stop-and-waste valve, indicating its dual purpose.

In case of a plumbing emergency, it's a good idea to have your house main shutoff valve labeled and see that all family members know where it's located. Often it's in the basement or crawlspace. However, in non-freezing climates both the main shutoff valve and water meter may be outdoors.

From the main shutoff, water runs in a pipe called a house main. First stop is the water softener, if you have one. Water for outdoor use, and often for toilets, bypasses the water softener via a hard water main. Smaller branches take off to outside faucets for yard watering.

Hot/Cold. The house main leads

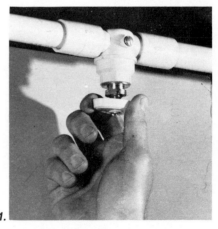

1.

1. Turning off the main shutoff for the house water supply system cuts off water to the whole house. It's usually located in the basement or crawlspace. Side drain screw lets the pipes be drained.

to near the water heater. There, the water supply system splits into the hot water and the cold water systems. One pipe supplies the water heater with cold water and is valved as it enters the heater. The pipe leaving the water heater begins the hot water supply system.

Fixtures. Both hot and cold water are routed to house appliances and fixtures by pipes called hot water and cold water mains. Branches from these mains lead to groups of fixtures and to large water-using fixtures such as kitchen sinks, laundries, bathtubs and showers. Pipes going up through walls are termed risers.

Correct pipe sizing is important to keep the hot-cold flow to a fixture uniform when water to another fixture is turned on or off. This way, no one fixture can rob the water intended for another.

Behind the wall (usually), in back of fixtures and appliances, are what are called air chambers. These consist of pipes a foot long and capped on the upper ends. Under pressure, water rises in the air chambers so formed, compressing the trapped air at its top. The purpose of air chambers is to cushion the shock of fast running water through the water supply system, as it is stopped abruptly when you turn off the faucet.

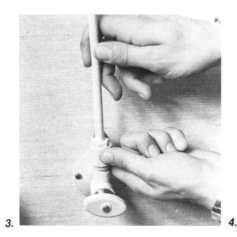
1.

2.

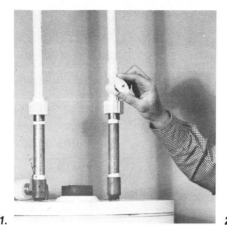
3.

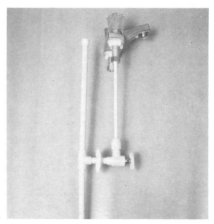
4.

1. Turning off the shutoff valve, located atop the hot water tank, stops cold water from entering the tank and hot water from flowing to fixtures.

2. Every hot water heater needs a temperature-pressure relief valve. Lifting the pump-type handle tests its operation.

3. Neatest, easiest way to connect house fixtures to the water supply is using a flexible Genova Poly Riser™. It pushes into a Genogrip™ fixture supply valve.

4. Water to the fixture can then be turned on or off using the valve. The tube leading from the tee is an air chamber to prevent water hammer.

Quick-acting solenoid water valves on washing machines and dishwashers turn off quite abruptly. Then, internal water supply system pressures can reach 500 psi and more, kicking out in all directions on the piping. Overpressures like these create a sound called water hammer, which is familiar to most owners of old houses. They also endanger the soundness of your water supply system. Air chambers do away with water hammer and the overpressures caused by it.

No faucet or water-using appliance should be without an air chamber on both the hot and cold supply.

Riser Tubes. In the best water supply systems each fixture is provided with shutoff valves either below it or under the floor beneath it. These valves, called fixture shutoffs, let you turn off either the hot or the cold water to the fixture in an emergency or for making repairs.

Fixtures such as sinks, lavatories and toilets are often served from wall or floor fixture shutoff valves or unvalved adapters through what are called riser tubes. These ⅜-inch diameter flexible pipes allow easy hookup between the water supply system and the fixture. They also permit quick disconnection in changing or modernizing of fixtures.

Automatic washing machines connect to hot and cold water spigots with hoses. The spigots should be turned off between uses.

Dishwashers connect directly to the hot water supply main. A valve is needed in the pipe so that the unit may be removed for service, if necessary, without disrupting the whole house water supply.

The water supply system ends at the fixture, or appliance.

DRAIN-WASTE-VENT SYSTEM

The drain-waste-vent, or simply DWV, system begins at the fixtures and appliances where the water supply system stops. Since drained water is not under pressure, the DWV piping must slope slightly toward where the waste water is supposed to go by gravity flow.

DWV fittings are designed with slightly-less-than-square (90°) turns to help the plumber maintain slope. Water flows from each fixture and appliance to the city sewer or to a private sewage disposal system in the yard. The DWV piping becomes ever larger as the collected wastes from more and more fixtures and appliances flow into it.

The first DWV pipe which leads waste away from the fixture is called a *waste pipe.* Toilets require large outflow pipes because of the great flow of water coming from them and the solids that must be carried along without clogging. Because of this, toilet drainage pipes are not called waste pipes, but rather are called *soil pipes.*

Stacks. Fixture waste pipes and toilets usually empty into what's called a stack, or soil stack. A stack is a vertical pipe that's open above the roof. At its lower end a stack leads into the building drain. Waste water flows to the bottom of the stack and into the building drain.

If it serves a toilet, a stack is called a main stack, or soil stack. Every house has at least one main stack, which measures 3 or 4 inches in diameter. If a stack does not serve a toilet, it's called a secondary stack or waste stack. Then it may measure only 1½ or even 2 inches.

Many houses have no need for secondary stacks; everything empties into the main one.

The building drain is a horizontal pipe--3 or 4 inches in diameter--that collects waste water from all the fixtures, including toilets, and leads it out of the house.

Once outside--5 feet away from the foundation to be exact--a building drain becomes the house sewer. All this occurs below ground level.

The house sewer pipe slopes to drain into a city sewer or private septic system.

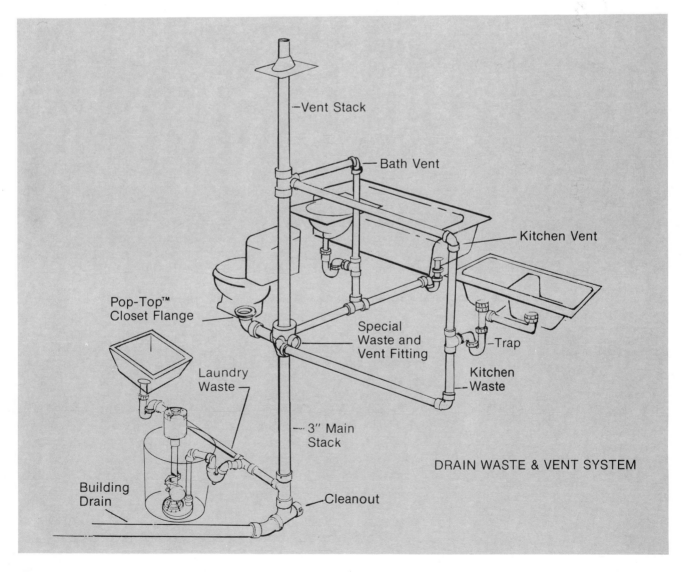

Vent Stack

Bath Vent

Kitchen Vent

Pop-Top™ Closet Flange

Special Waste and Vent Fitting

Trap

Laundry Waste

Kitchen Waste

3" Main Stack

DRAIN WASTE & VENT SYSTEM

Building Drain

Cleanout

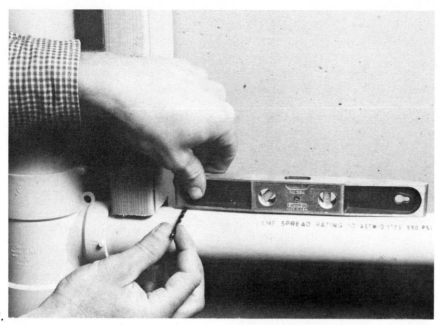

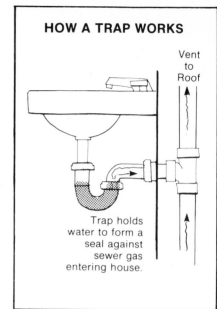

HOW A TRAP WORKS

Vent to Roof

Trap holds water to form a seal against sewer gas entering house.

1.

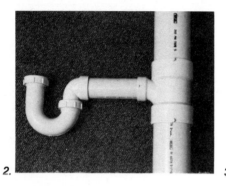

2.

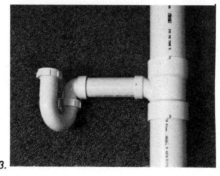

3.

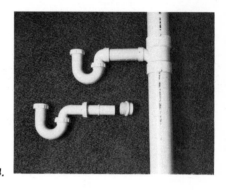

4.

1. Drain-waste-vent pipes should slope slightly to drain. Here a 3/16" drill placed under the low end of a 9" level centers the bubble indicating a 1/4" per foot slope.

2. Genova P-trap solvent welds directly to stub-out directly behind fixture. Water drains away through the pipe below the tee. The trap is vented through the vent pipe above tee.

3. Swiveling J-bend on trap lets it be pivoted right or left to meet the fixture's drain pipe. Tightened, the trap's slip-nut seals water inside. This trap is made of polypropylene.

4. Two styles of sink/lavatory traps offered by Genova out-perform metal traps, yet they install similarly. One installs with a slip-nut; the other solvent welds to the waste pipe.

Traps. The DWV system contains a couple of refinements along the way that were skipped over in describing it. One is the trap. A trap is a water-filled, U-shaped pipe that will allow water and wastes to pass through, but prevents gases and vermin inside the DWV system from slipping backwards into the house. Every appliance and every fixture must have a trap. Without traps, your house soon would smell like the inside of a sewer.

Toilets contain built-in traps because their intricate bowl passages are trap-shaped. The water you see in the bowl is part of a toilet's trap seal. In fact when a toilet finishes flushing, the trap's siphon action often depletes most of its trap-sealing water. For this reason, a toilet tank's fill mechanism is designed to replenish the lost trap-sealing water as the tank refills.

Other fixtures and appliances use separate traps. Traps for sinks and lavatories are either P-shaped or S-shaped, but both contain a U-shaped trap section. These traps hide underneath fixtures. One end of the trap connects to a tailpiece coming out of the fixture drain. The trap must be at least as large as the tailpiece. The other end slips into the DWV system's waste pipe. Slip-nut connections with soft ring-type gaskets make slip joints both water- and gas-tight.

Tub and shower traps may be drum-type (more costly) or else large-sized P-traps. They're located in or beneath the floor under the fixture.

Wherever a trap is located, access must be provided for cleaning should it become clogged. Toilet and sink-lavatory traps can be cleaned from above, through the fixture drain. Some bathtub and shower traps are accessible for cleaning through the drain; some aren't. These are designed for cleaning from above through a hole in the floor or from below in the basement or crawl-space.

The best P- and S-traps are built with a cleanout opening at the lowest point of the dip. Removal of the cleanout plug allows draining and direct access for cleaning.

Vents. The necessity for traps brings on still another plumbing necessity, venting. As you may know, water rushing along by gravity through a pipe creates a suction or vacuum at the high end of the pipe above it. This is called siphon action. Siphon action is powerful enough to suck all the water out of a trap and leave it nearly dry, as happens in a toilet bowl after a flush. But, since other fixtures and appliances aren't designed to replace siphoned-off trap water as a toilet is, some means of preventing trap siphoning must be built into the DWV system. This is accomplished by venting the system to outside air. Venting inside the house would work too, but then sewer gases would escape into the house. Thus, venting is done outside above the roof.

Venting also prevents any pressurization in the DWV system or sewer system from building to the point where it could force past a trap's water seal. Every trap in a plumbing system should be vented.

Reventing. Now things get more complicated. If the waste pipe from a fixture is short enough or large enough, a fixture's trap can be both drained and vented through the same pipe. This is called wet-venting. All fixtures are wet-vented for a short distance. The length of wet-venting is limited by plumbing codes and what will work in use. If a stack isn't located close

behind the fixture, the wet-vented distance may be too long. Then, alternate venting must be provided. This may be in the form of an additional stack closer to the fixture or a branch vent called a revent.

Because adding an additional stack up through the roof can be more costly than reventing, the revent is most often used.

A revent is a vent-only pipe leading upward from the fixture waste pipe and bending as necessary to connect into a stack above the point where the highest fixture waste pipe enters it. The branch vent stack connection may or may not be into the same stack the fixture drains into. It doesn't matter. The trap is vented.

Stacks and vents usually are made from the same size pipe as is used for draining the fixture. Sometimes a size or two smaller vent pipe is permitted. No vent or no waste pipe is smaller than 1¼ inch. More recently, 1½ inch is the smallest size used.

HOW A VENT WORKS

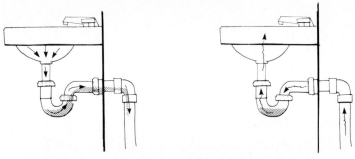

With no vent, trap water siphons off leaving too little in trap to stop sewer gases.

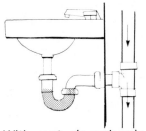

With vent, air rushes in to prevent siphoning of trap, gas seal remains intact.

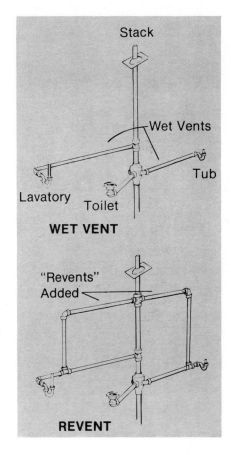

WET VENT

REVENT

HOW A TOILET WORKS

Water rushes in from tank and into bowl starting siphon action

Water Supply Fittings

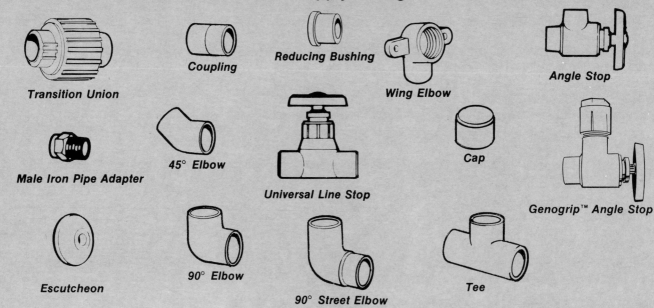

Transition Union

Coupling

Reducing Bushing

Wing Elbow

Angle Stop

Male Iron Pipe Adapter

45° Elbow

Universal Line Stop

Cap

Genogrip™ Angle Stop

Escutcheon

90° Elbow

90° Street Elbow

Tee

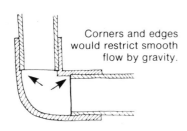

Corners and edges would restrict smooth flow by gravity.

WATER SUPPLY FITTING

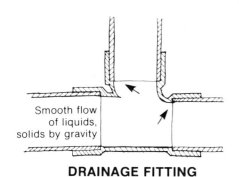

Smooth flow of liquids, solids by gravity

DRAINAGE FITTING

1.

1. A horizontal run of drainage pipe should have a cleanout opening at the high end. Genova's Twist-Lok™ plug slips into a tee or wye bend, locks with a twist. No tools are needed.

Cleanouts. Another specialty of the DWV system is the cleanout. Its purpose is to permit the removal of inside-the-system stoppages caused by grease buildups or other problems sometimes associated with draining wastes by gravity flow. Every horizontal drainage run-- but not vent run--must be provided with access for cleaning it. This is often by a cleanout opening at the higher end of the run.

Cleanouts are made with special cleanout fittings. Genova Twist-Lok™ is the best system on the market for this. Genova DWV fittings are made to accept gasketed Twist-Lok™ cleanout covers. The on-off connection is made easily by hand without tools of any kind. There are no threads to corrode and jam up.

The sewer line leading away from the house also needs an accessible cleanout opening for rodding it out, should it become blocked.

Drain-Waste-Vent Fittings

Reducing Bushing

22½° Elbow

Reducing Coupling

Floor Strainer

Wye

Bell Trap

Vent Tee

45° Street Elbow

Reducing Wye

Special Waste and Vent Fitting

Pop-Top™ Closet Flange

Male Adapter

Fitting Adapter

45° Elbow

90° Vent Elbow

Sanitary Tee

Twist-Lok™ Plug

Coupling

Plumbing Fittings. Fittings used for carrying away waste water by gravity flow are built differently from those for water supply use. They're called drainage fittings. Drainage fittings are designed with gentle bends and curving inner surfaces that reduce resistance to flow. This also helps solids to pass through the fittings more easily.

Common water supply fittings-- elbows, tees and couplings-- make abrupt changes in direction. Elbows come in 45- and 90-degrees. Differences in pipe size are accommodated by what are called reducers.

Changes in pipe type are done with adapters. For example, to go from threaded steel pipe to solvent welded vinyl pipe takes a threads-to-solvent-weld adapter. Some fittings combine a change in direction or change in size along with some other function, such as in an adapter, elbow or a reducing tee.

From these basic water supply fittings numerous other special purpose fittings are produced to make the plumber's installation of them easier and better.

The common DWV-type fittings are elbows (sometimes called bends), tees, wyes and couplings. Elbows come as 22½-degree, 45-degree, 60-degree and 90-degree. Tees make a 90-degree angle; wyes make a 45-degree angle. DWV fittings, too, offer reducers, adapters and other special fittings for an easier, better job.

One of these is the closet (toilet) flange, which couples the bottom of the toilet effectively to the DWV system. Genova's Pop-Top™ toilet flange comes with a knock-out cover to keep debris out of the DWV system until you're ready to install the toilet. It also serves to plug the toilet opening for the DWV system's static water-fill test (described on page 88).

QUALITY PLUMBING

Almost every locality in the United States has a plumbing code. A plumbing code is simply a set of rules that the governing body would like followed in making plumbing installations. Local codes vary slightly, but their implied intent is to safeguard community health. Although codes are important, remember that in recent years

they have been hard-put to keep abreast of changing technologies, so some codes have become outmoded.

Genova's plumbing materials are widely approved by code-writing bodies. Some have been used for more than 20 years around the world.

If you run into an out-of-date code that seems to bar vinyl plumbing, you can ask the chief plumbing inspector for a variance in your case. Or, you can interpret the code's provisions as they apply to your job and proceed in the manner you judge best.

YOU CAN DO IT

Contrary to popular notions promoted by trade groups, plumbing is neither tough to do nor complicated. Nor does plumbing require skills gained only in long apprentice programs. (Those apprentice programs spend days and days teaching how to master the intricacies of working with hard to handle materials, ones you can avoid.) If the right materials are used, plumbing can be quite simple. As far as I'm concerned, Genova is it.

Glossary of Plumbing Terms

Air gap--In a drainage system, often used in a dishwasher's discharge in which the appliance discharges through air into a receptacle. Used to meet codes that prohibit pressurized discharge into a DWV system.

Air gap--In a water supply system, the distance between the faucet outlet and the flood rim of the basin it discharges into. Used to prevent contamination of the water supply by back-siphonage.

Anti-siphon--Term applied to valves or other devices that eliminate back-siphonage.

Backflow--Reverse flow of water or other liquids into water supply pipes carrying potable water. Back-siphonage is a type of backflow.

Backflow-preventer--A device or means to prevent backflow.

Back-siphonage--Backflow of contaminated water by negative pressure in the potable water system.

Backwater valve--A one-way valve installed in the house drain or sewer that prevents flooding of low-level fixtures by backing up of the sewer.

Ball cock--Toilet tank water supply valve, which is controlled by a float ball. Usually of the anti-siphon type.

Branch--Any part of a piping system other than a riser, main or stack.

Branch vent--(See revent.)

Building drain--The lowest house piping that receives discharge from stack, waste and other drainage pipes and carries it to the building sewer outside the house.

Building sewer--Normally begins five feet outside the foundation of the house. Carries house sewage underground to the sewer or private disposal system.

Building trap--Device installed in the building drain to prevent gases from the sewer from circulating inside the house DWV system.

Cesspool--Lined or covered excavation in the ground that receives domestic wastes from the drainage system. Retains organic matter and solids; lets liquids seep into the ground through its porous bottom and sides.

Chlorination--Application of chlorine to water or treated sewage to disinfect or accomplish other biological or chemical results.

Cistern--Small covered tank chiefly used for storing rain water for domestic use other than drinking. Usually placed underground.

Cleanout--Accessible opening in the drainage system used for removing obstructions.

Code--Regulations adopted by local administrative agencies having jurisdiction.

Cross connection--Physical connection between potable water supply and any non-potable water source.

Distribution box--Concrete or other receptacle in the ground with one inlet located higher than two or more outlets. Used to equally divide the quantity of septic tank effluent among various branches of a seepage system.

Drain--Any pipe that carries waste water or water-borne wastes in a building drainage system.

Drainage system--All the piping that carries sewage, rainwater or other liquid wastes to the point of disposal or sewer.

Dry well--Underground excavation used for leaching of other than sewage into the ground.

Effluent--The liquid discharge from a septic tank.

Fixture supply--Water supply pipe that connects a fixture to a branch water supply pipe or directly to a main water supply pipe.

Fixture unit, drainage (dfu)--A measure of the probable discharge into the drainage system by various plumbing fixtures. In general, on small systems, one dfu approximates one cubic foot of water a minute.

Fixture unit, water supply (sfu)--A measure of the probable water demand by various plumbing fixtures.

Flood level rim--The edge of a fixture receptacle from which water overflows.

Flush valve--A device at the bottom of a toilet tank for flushing it.

Grade--The fall or slope of a line pipes in reference to the horizontal. Is usually expressed as fall in fractions of an inch per foot of pipe length.

Leaching pit--(See seepage pit.)

Liquid waste--Discharge from any fixture, appliance, etc., that does not contain fecal matter.

Main--Principal pipe to which branches are connected.

Main vent (or stack)--Principal vent to which branch vents may be connected.

Nonpotable water--Water that is not safe for drinking.

Pitch--(See grade.)

Plumbing--The practice, materials and fixtures used in installation, maintenance, extension and alteration of all piping, fixtures, plumbing appliances and plumbing appurtenances in connection with any of the following: sanitary drainage, storm drainage and venting systems, and public or private water supply systems within any structure, building or conveyance. Covers the extensions of these lines to no more than five feet beyond the foundation walls of the structure. Not included are gas piping, heating or cooling piping and piping for fire sprinklers and standpipes.

Plumbing fixture--A receptacle or device either permanently or temporarily connected to the water supply system and which demands a supply of water therefrom. Discharges used water or wastes directly or indirectly to the drainage system.

Plumbing system--Includes water supply and distribution pipes; plumbing fixtures and traps; drain, waste and vent pipes; and building drains including their respective connections, devices and appurtenances within a building or structure to a point no more than five feet beyond the foundation walls.

Potable water--Water free from impurities in amounts sufficient to cause disease or harmful psychological effects. Conforms to the requirements of the U. S. Public Health Service Drinking Water Standards or regulations of the public health authority having jurisdiction.

Revent--A pipe installed specifically to vent a fixture trap. Connects with the vent system above the fixture served.

Riser--Short, vertical pipe in the water supply system leading from the main.

Riser tube--Short, flexible tube that connects fixture to the water supply system.

Rough-in--The installation of parts of the plumbing system that can be done before installation of the fixtures. Includes drainage, water supply and vent piping and the necessary fixture supports.

Sanitary sewer--A sewer that carries sewage but not storm, surface or ground water.

Seepage field--Arrangement of perforated or open-joint piping underground that permits septic tank effluent to leach into the surrounding porous soil.

Seepage well or pit--Same purpose as seepage field but confined to a hole in the ground.

Septic tank--A water-tight receptacle that receives raw sewage from the house sewer, digests organic matter retained in it and allows liquid effluent to discharge to a seepage field or pit.

Sewage--Any liquid waste containing animal or vegetable matter in suspension or solution. May include liquids containing chemicals in solution.

Sewage ejector--Device for lifting sewage by entraining it in a high velocity stream of air or water.

Slip-joint--Joint used primarily on the fixture side of a trap made tight with a rubber or plastic washer and a slip-nut.

Stack--Any vertical line of drain, waste or vent pipes that vents above the roof.

Stack venting--Method of venting a fixture through the stack.

Storm sewer--A sewer used for carrying rain or surface water, cooling water and similar liquid wastes.

Subsoil drain--A drain that collects subsurface water and carries it to a place of disposal.

Sump--A tank or pit for sewage or liquid wastes located below the normal grade of the gravity system and which must be emptied by mechanical means.

Sump pump--Automatic water pump powered by an electric motor for the removal of drainage, other than raw sewage, from a sump, pit or low point.

Supports--Devices for supporting and securing pipe, fixtures and equipment.

Temperature-pressure relief valve--Also called T & P valve. Installed atop the hot water heater tank to relieve the buildup of dangerous temperatures or pressures inside the tank should its heating system fail to turn off automatically.

Trap--Fitting or device used to provide a liquid seal to keep sewer gases out of the house without affecting the outflow of sewage or waste water through it.

Trap seal--The vertical distance between the crown weir and the top of the dip of a trap.

Vacuum--Any pressure less than that exerted by the atmosphere.

Vacuum breaker--Device used in water supply line to let in air and prevent back-siphonage. Some are designed to operate under line pressure, others are not.

Vent pipe--Part of the vent system.

Vent stack--Vertical vent pipe installed to provide circulation of air to and from the drainage system.

Vent system--A pipe or pipes installed to provide a flow of air to or from a drainage system or to provide a circulation of air within such a system to protect trap seals from siphonage and back pressure.

Waste--Liquid-borne waste free of fecal matter.

Waste pipe--A pipe that carries only waste.

Water closet--A toilet.

Water main--Water supply pipe for public use.

Water supply system--The water service entrance pipe, water distributing pipes, and the necessary connecting pipes and fittings, control valves and appurtenances in or adjacent to the building or premises.

Well--Driven, bored or dug hole in the ground from which water is pumped.

Wet-vent--A vent that also receives the discharge of wastes other than from water closets.

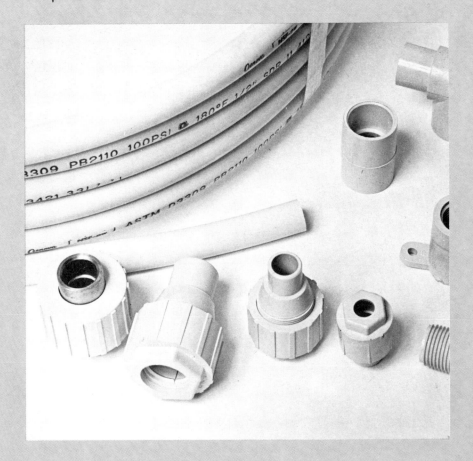

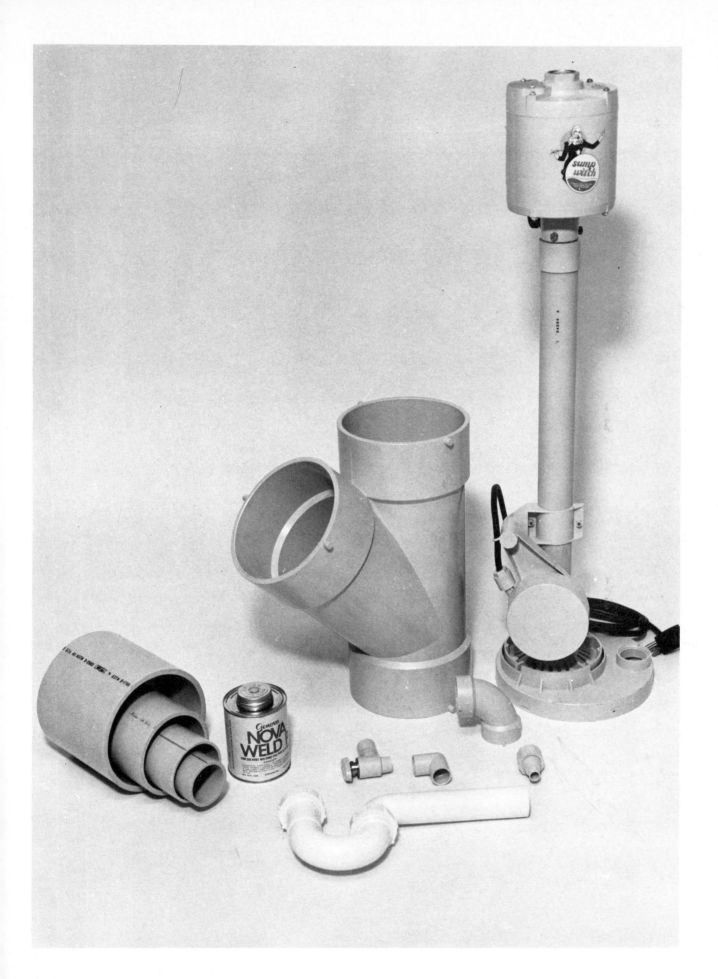

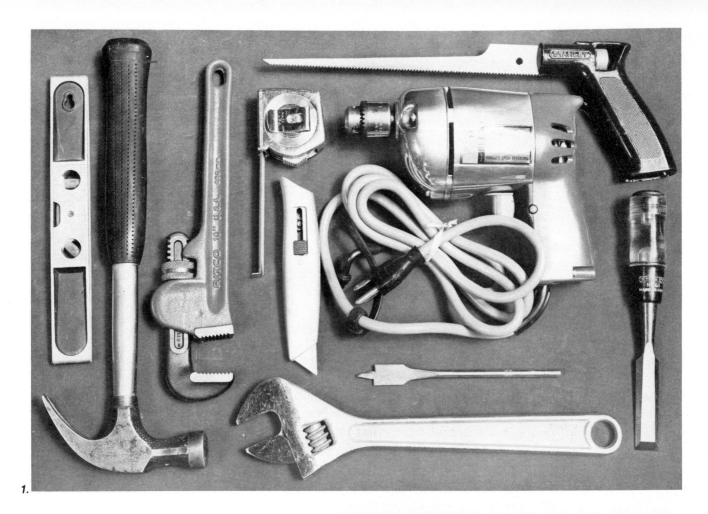

1.

1. Tools needed for a complete Genova CPVC or PB water supply installation are few. Most are needed for working on house framing. Pocket knife, rule and handsaw will handle the piping itself. You'll also need goggles.

2. Almost any fine-toothed saw you have will cut CPVC pipe with ease. It need not be a hacksaw. Cuts should be square. Holding the pipe in a vise is one way; hand-holding's okay, too.

3. Pair of smooth bores. Not muzzle-loaders, but pipes. Genova CPVC (left) and PB are so smooth inside that their flow rates surpass those of metal piping. What's more, hard water scale won't build.

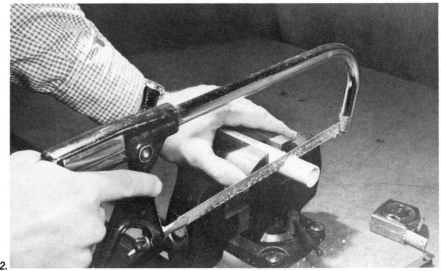

2.

3.

Hot & Cold Water Piping

The smart way to new or add-on plumbing for your house is with chlorinated polyvinyl chloride (CPVC). CPVC is a tougher version of older PVC, and polybutylene (PB) is a heat-resistant flexible thermoplastic, recent in the plumbing field.

Using Genova CPVC and PB pipe and fittings, plus a handsaw and some ordinary common sense, you have all the ingredients for doing a first class plumbing job.

CPVC comes as light-beige-colored rigid vinyl pipe and a wide array of fittings to serve both hot and cold water supply. It's available in ¾- and ½-inch diameters in 10 foot lengths. You can cut it with an ordinary hand-saw, join it by easy solvent welding.

PB comes as flexible beige pipe for hot and cold water supply. It's available in 1-, ¾-, ½- and ¼-inch inside diameter in 100-foot coils and all but 1-inch in the 25-foot coils. Cut it with a knife and join it with PB/CPVC adapters plus regular Genova CPVC solvent weld fittings. Some Genova CPVC fittings come with PB adapters already incorporated.

Both CPVC and PB are code-accepted practically everywhere. CPVC conforms to the renowned American Society for Testing and Materials (ASTM) D2846. PB conforms to ASTM D3309. Both are accepted by the Federal Housing Administration. What this means to you is assurance that your Genova water supply system will last.

Pipe sizes. Genova water systems are characterized by their use of special high temperature thermoplastics. Sizing goes by copper water tube sizes. That means pipe size is measured nominally by inside diameter (I.D.).

Thus, the inside diameters of ½-inch CPVC and PB pipe measure about ½ inch. Their outside diameters (O.D.) are ⅝ inch.

Similarly, ¾-inch CPVC and PB pipes scale about ¾ inch I.D. and ⅞ inch O.D.

The ⅜-inch polybutylene pipe actually measures ¼ inch I.D. and ⅜ inch O.D.

Benefits. The insides of CPVC and PB pipes and fittings come so smooth that they offer much less resistance to water flow than does galvanized steel water pipe. Therefore, smaller sizes of CPVC and PB pipe can do the same job that requires larger sizes of steel pipe.

Energy-saving, too, CPVC and PB pipes and fittings retard heat loss in a hot water supply system far better than metal piping. Genova piping robs almost no heat from your hot water system. Thus, YOU get just about all of it. And once hot, water stays hot longer within the self-insulating system.

In cold water systems this same self-insulating effect works for you too. It greatly reduces pipe sweating.

Vinyl and polybutylene have another benefit: they don't corrode. With no buildup of corrosion, pipe bores stay full sized. This allows an old Genova system to enjoy the same good flow characteristics it had when new.

Still another advantage, CPVC and PB are nonconductors of electricity. Thus, they're free from electrolysis that can destroy a metal water system. When dissimilar metals, such as galvanized steel in a water heater and a copper piping system go together, the resulting dielectric action eats away at the walls of the system. And worse, hard water acts like the electrolyte in your car battery to tear down metals.

The nonconducting qualities of Genova materials greatly extend the life of the whole plumbing system by preventing electrolysis.

When you work with solvent welded CPVC joints in your house, you'll doubly appreciate how they join without a torch. Making up sweat soldered pipes by torching has caused more than one house fire, started while the water was turned off.

Besides all this, a Genova water supply system costs less than others. It's a wise choice for new or add-on plumbing.

CPVC. Chlorinated polyvinyl chloride is part of the family of rigid PVC vinyls made tougher and more heat resistant by adding an extra chloride atom to the PVC molecule. This makes it valuable for both hot and cold water pressure piping. CPVC meets all the requirements of the National Sanitation Foundation (NSF) for potable water conveyance.

Fixtures, plumbing appliances and appurtenances seldom come ready to solvent weld a CPVC pipe to. Most often they're fitted with threaded tappings. So, at the well, water main, appliances, fixtures and other plumbing devices you adapt CPVC to the threaded fittings found there. Genova's complete line of fittings let you connect to just about anything.

Fitness of fittings. One thing you'll like about working with Genova products is the wide selection of *500 Series* fittings. These join, adapt, reduce, go around bends, divert, turn off, couple, whatever needs doing.

If your dealer doesn't stock all of the fittings, ask him to show you the Genova catalog so you can pick out what you need. Then your dealer can order them for you. Some are shown on page 10.

While we're on the subject of dealers and their stocks of fittings, this caution: Make sure all the fittings and pipes you buy are the same brand. This is important. Not all stores stock fittings this way. Some even stock different colors of pipes and fittings manufactured by various firms. Don't buy your plumbing system this way. You want a working system, not just a collection of parts. And, the system is no better than its parts.

Although there is an industry standard for outside pipe dimensions or inside fitting dimensions or for the clearance between the two, the tolerances are very wide. Each manufacturer designs his own products to work together, but not necessarily to work with those of any other manufacturer. If you mix your fittings, this can get you into trouble. Here's how:

Genova pioneered CPVC pipe and fittings a long time ago. Even though others have since followed Genova's lead, Genova's close tolerances in pipe and fitting sizes haven't been successfully emulated. Other manufacturer's CPVC pipes coming off the extrusion machines vary in size. For that reason their fitting sockets need to be made larger to accommodate the largest pipe. If you happen to pick up a smallish ½-inch pipe, say, and a largeish ½-inch fitting and try to solvent weld them together, you start with a very sloppy fit. The looseness may be too much to be overcome by the solvent cement. Then you'll end up with a leaking joint.

It isn't worth the risk. I recommend that you use ONLY Genova pipes and fittings.

Genova rigidly controls its pipe to much closer tolerances than any other manufacturer. Thus, Genova fittings can be held to a uniformly snug fit with the pipe. This ensures leak-free joints. In fact, a leaking joint in a Genova-plumbed CPVC house proves rare.

So, don't ask your dealer whether the yellow pipe works with the gray fitting. Simply look for the word Genova, then you're assured of compatibility.

These precautions apply to PVC drain-waste-vent pipe and fittings as well as to water supply. All Genova vinyl piping products are produced in the natural color of vinyl, a pleasant, quality-denoting beige color. This color is your assurance of quality because it is impossible to "fill" the fitting or pipe with foreign substances such as chalk. Many of the profusion of white-colored plumbing fittings and pipe are chalk filled.

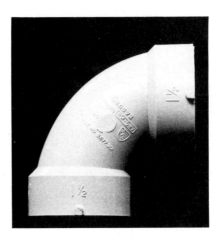

Solvent welding. Solvents used in making the CPVC joint cements make another part of the quality story. For use with Genova CPVC pipe and fittings use ONLY Genova solvents. They're the only pipe fitting manufacturer who makes their own cements. Genova cements contain tetra hydro-furan (THF), a costly but effective ingredient, that many cut-rate solvent manufacturers skimp on. Some solvents sell for less than Genova's, but you'll get the strongest joints with Genova. A ruined carpet or ceiling caused by a leaking joint isn't worth the small saving of a cheap solvent. And once joined, you can't "unsolder" it.

Making successful, leak-free joints with Genova materials is easy. It's much simpler than

1.

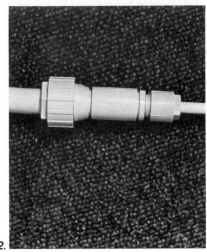

2.

1. Genova's specially developed transition fitting, which adapts metal pipe to CPVC, lets each pipe type expand and contract with heating and cooling at its own rate across a neoprene rubber washer.

2. Reduction in pipe sizes, here going from ½" PB to ⅜" PB, is done with a ½" x ⅜" bushing inserted at the right end of a ½" coupling. Hand-tightened Genogrip™ adapters fit the PB pipe to its CPVC fittings.

3. Using Genova CPVC fittings and CPVC/PB adapters in various sizes, you can make polybutylene tubing do just about anything you wish. Stackable tee at right, branches ½" CPVC to ⅜" PB, can be ganged.

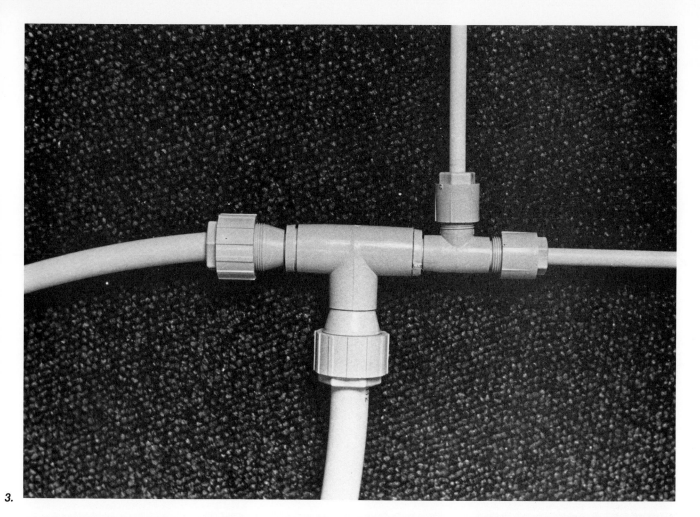

3.

4.

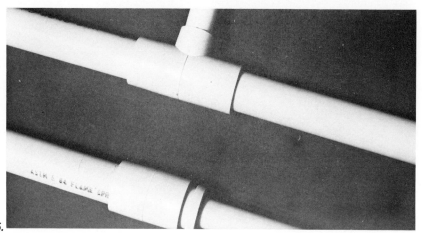

5.

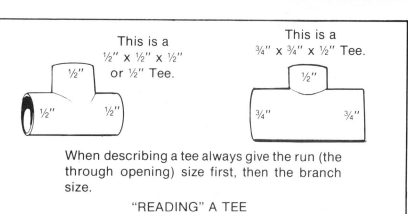

4. Here's how a reducing bushing works. This Genova Part No. 50275, ¾" x ½" bushing solvent welds into a standard ¾" fitting, letting ½" CPVC pipe be used in the fitting (here a coupling).

5. Some CPVC fittings are designed for reducing pipe sizes, such as the ¾" x ¾" x ½" tee at top. Others are made into reducing fittings as desired by adding a reducing bushing to a fitting socket.

This is a
½" x ½" x ½"
or ½" Tee.

½"

½"   ½"

This is a
¾" x ¾" x ½" Tee.

½"

¾"   ¾"

When describing a tee always give the run (the through opening) size first, then the branch size.

"READING" A TEE

joining sweated or threaded pipes and fittings.

Genova President, R. M. Williams, says, "If you do it right, it's impossible to get a leak." And that's what I've found in years of use.

The Genova people have long advocated the two-step solvent welding process. By two-step they mean the use of a cleaner (or primer, if you prefer) and then a solvent cement on every joint. It's the best antileak insurance there is.

One trouble: Solvent welding is so easy that you're tempted to skip a step here and there. Don't, because the doped joint is permanent once assembled. There's no way to back up and perform the missing step. So, follow directions--they're printed on the can.

First, inspect the fitting and pipe end for gouges. Then clean the joint with Novaclean™. Made with THF, tetra hydro-furan, and MEK, methylethyl ketone, the cleaner's purpose is to remove dirt, grease, oil and other joint destroying residues on mating joint surfaces. Although you may not see the residue, it's there. Apply Novaclean™ with a clean cloth around the outside of the pipe end and inside the fitting socket. Do it before applying solvent cement and let it dry before proceeding. Never use Novaclean™ to thin solvent cement.

Then follow with fresh Novaweld C™ for solvent welding CPVC pipe and fittings. Novaweld C™ also may be used on ordinary PVC cold water pipe in outdoor applications. While Novaweld C™ may be used to solvent weld larger PVC

drain-waste-vent pipes and fittings, Novaweld P™ is recommended for that. (Do not use Novaweld P™ on CPVC joints.) Another choice for solvent welding is Genova All Purpose Cement. It can be used on CPVC, PVC, ABS & Styrene.

At 24 hours old, the pipe will burst before the fitting will fail.

Also, don't try to solvent weld polybutylene pipe. PB cannot be solvent welded with ANY cement. It must be joined with special adapters made by Genova.

The chief cause of a rare, leaky CPVC joint is too little cement. Be generous with solvent cement. The handy dauber that comes with the can of cement is large enough to handle the joining of all water supply pipe sizes. No brush is needed with them.

1.

SOLVENT WELDING CPVC PIPE

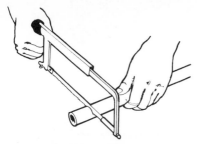

1. Cut to length squarely and allow for makeup dimension (depth of fitting socket). Use a fine-tooth saw or a pipe cutter with a special vinyl cutting wheel.

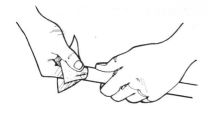

2. Remove all burrs on pipe end using sandpaper or a knife.

3. With a clean rag, wipe Novaclean™ on pipe and socket.

4. Follow immediately with Novaweld C™ or Novaweld All Purpose™ application. Apply Novaweld™ solvent liberally on pipe and sparingly on socket.

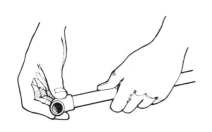

5. Quickly push the pipe into the socket with a slight twisting motion until it bottoms. Adjust alignment of fitting immediately, before the solvent sets up.

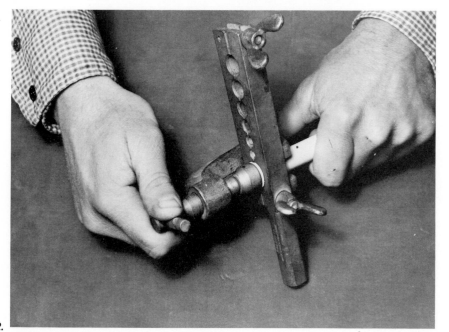

1. Both CPVC and PB come in copper tubing sizes and can be flared to adapt to standard flare fittings. This can enable easy connection at faucets, other fixtures and appliances.

2. To flare a Genova pipe use a standard flaring tool in the usual way. Make sure that the end to be flared is squarely and cleanly cut and warmed in boiling water to prevent cracking. Successful flares have clean edges without cracks where tube was expanded. Don't forget to install the flare nut before flaring.

2.

TRANSITION FITTINGS

Whenever connecting a Genova water supply system to threaded or sweat soldered metal pipes and fittings, Genova transition fittings should be used. Although ordinary threaded CPVC adapters work okay on cold water supplies, leaks may develop if they are used for hot water lines. The reason? Metal and vinyl have differing rates of expansion as they're heated and cooled. Ordinary adapters don't allow for this. Specially designed Genova transition fittings present two faces that meet across a rubber gasket. Each face can expand or contract at its own rate without affecting the other. The transition fittings are part of the Genova *500 Series* product line. They also perform the function of unions, letting a connection be disassembled at any time.

1.

1. Genova Genogrip™ adapters (top left ¾", right ½") solvent weld directly into standard fittings and adapt mechanically to both polybutylene tubing and copper tubing by utilizing either of the special gripper rings supplied. Genova hot water transition unions (bottom row) join metal pipes to CPVC with complete success, allow easy take-apart by hand. Left to right: ½" male pipe, ¾" male pipe, ¾" female pipe, ½" female pipe.

2. To use a hot water transition union for sweat soldered copper tubing, install the handnut over the tube and slide it back at least 18" from the joint. Then solder the fitting onto the tube.

3. When the fitting cools the adapter can be assembled with its neoprene washer between the metal and vinyl parts. Tighten the handnut firmly to seal the joint. Then you can take off with CPVC pipe.

4. To adapt CPVC pipe to threaded pipes, simply install the proper sized hot water transition union on the threaded side. Tighten, finishing with a pipe wrench. Teflon™ tape helps threaded joints to seal tightly.

4.

2.

3.

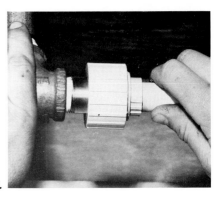

5.

5. With the hot water transition union installed, take off with CPVC pipe, solvent welding instead of threading the joints. Apply solvent to the fitting socket of the adapter, then to the pipe end.

6. Then push the pipe all the way into the fitting to complete the solvent welded joint. You're now started with CPVC and can continue using it to the end of the run without further adapters.

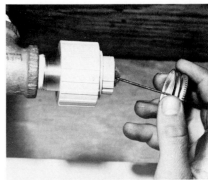

6.

RUNNING PIPES

When measuring for pipe runs, no matter what type of pipe, you must allow for the distances taken up by the fittings. This is called makeup. If you forget makeup, you are liable to cut the pipe too short or too long.

Measurements are made more complex because the pipe ends slip into the fitting sockets.

Simplifying the whole matter is the table of fitting makeup dimensions. This shows, for 1/2- and 3/4-inch fittings, how much to subtract for that fitting when measuring from the center of the fitting to the end of the pipe that slips into it. Always subtract for center-to-end makeup.

For example, if you're branching down to meet a water heater tapping from a water supply main with 3/4-inch CPVC pipe, you'd stop the main just 9/16 inch (from 3/4" tee in table) short of the centerline of the branch pipe's centerline. When you later solvent weld a 3/4-inch tee and its down-pipe, it should align with the water heater's top tapping.

Don't forget that many runs of pipe have fittings at both ends to allow for in your makeup calculations.

Another way of laying out a job is to position the fittings on the floor spaced as they would be and then measure face to face of each pair of fittings for pipes that will join them. Then you must add to the pipe length the depth of the fitting sockets on both ends. Allow for socket depth as follows:

    1/2-inch fittings--1/2 inch
    3/4-inch fittings--11/16 inch

While center-to-end makeup is subtracted from required pipe length, remember to add socket depth to required pipe length.

In doing the job, it's a good idea to dry-assemble the pipe and fittings and check for fit before you solvent weld them. Don't forget to take apart all of the joints later and solvent weld them though. If you forget any, you'll have leaks that must be disassembled, dried and solvent welded.

PROPER DESIGN

All water supply systems must be designed to function within the limitations of the materials used to build them. Vinyl is no exception. While it's rated to withstand 100 psi water pressure at 180° F, CPVC will actually take more than this. However, the system should be designed to stay within these limits.

The use of air chambers at all fixtures and water using appliances is a must. If not to avoid plumbing noises, then use air chambers to protect the system from the excessive pressures created by water hammer.

CPVC and PB pipes should not be restrained against thermal expansion and contraction. To provide for some movement, do the following:

1. Always use Genova pipe hangers to support your pipes. These hold the pipe snugly to the framing, yet permit end-wise movement. They also will not cut into the pipe. Use one support at every other joist, or 32 inches on center.

2. Never install long runs of CPVC pipe touching walls or framing. Leave a little space at the end of a run for expansion.

3. Make one-foot doglegs (offsets) in overly long runs of CPVC pipe, those more than 35 feet long. These will bend enough to take up expansion.

4. CPVC risers branching off of CPVC mains should be un-bound and long enough from the main to where they extend through the floor or ceiling to accommodate slight movement of the main. An 8-inch distance should do the trick. PB risers have no such requirement because they're flexible.

GENOVA CPVC FITTING MAKEUP DIMENSIONS		
	Center-to-End Makeup	
Fitting	1/2"	3/4"
90° Elbow, Tee, Reducing Tee	3/8"	9/16"
90° Street Elbow (Street Side)		5/8"
Coupling	1/16"	1/16"
Line Stop	15/16"	13/16"
Union	5/8"	9/16"

(for other fittings take actual measurements)

1. Support CPVC pipes every 32" (every other joist) with Genova tubing straps. Available for both ¾" and ½" CPVC pipe, these hold the pipe firmly to framing and will not cut the pipe, yet the pipe is free to slide back and forth with thermal expansion and contraction. Risers coming off of mains should be long enough to flex with the end-wise movement and keep from strain.

2. Ends of long pipe runs should not be too close to framing. CPVC pipe needs about ¼" per 10' length to expand as it becomes hot.

1.

2.

3.

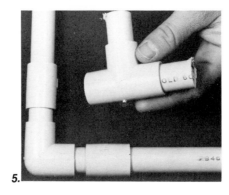

4.

5.

1. When installing a gas- or oil-fired water heater with a CPVC or PB hot water system, protect the pipes from conducted burner heat by threading a pair of 8" to 11" galvanized steel nipples into the heater.

2. Before threading a ¾" Genova CPVC (Part No. 530401) transition adapter onto the steel nipples, wrap one turn of Teflon™ plumber's tape around the threads to make a tight joint. Tape is neater than thread compound.

3. Go on up from the heater to reach the hot and cold water mains. A Genova (Part No. 530151) line stop installed in the cold water line with its flow arrow pointing down lets you turn off the hot water to the heater.

4. Now you can install the hot and cold water mains in basement, crawlspace or attic, solvent welding as you go. Heat resistant CPVC serves for both hot and cold water lines.

5. If you goof and install the wrong fitting or by some chance get a leaky joint, it's easy to fix. Simply saw out the wrong section of pipe and install a new section using couplings to join it in.

WATER HEATER

All hot water heaters, as described in the first chapter, need an approved temperature pressure relief valve. On modern heaters this threads into a ¾-inch tapping atop the heater. On older units without the tapping, a galvanized steel tee is placed in the hot water line coming out of the heater tank above the unit and the relief valve installed in the tee.

No matter how installed, the relief valve should have its temperature sensing probe reaching down inside the water tank. A CPVC pipe can extend from the relief valve to a handy drain.

You should also use two galvanized steel nipples 8 to 11 inches long coming off the top of a gas-fired or oil-fired water heater (see photos). This is to keep conducted heat built up by long burner runs from reaching the CPVC transition fittings. You can connect CPVC transition adapters directly to the tappings of an electric heater.

The water heater's temperature selector may be set for any desired heat range. Usually these are given as "Warm," "Medium," and "Hot," corresponding approximately to 140, 160 and 180 degrees F. Naturally, the lower you set the dial the more fuel you'll save. Try the lowest setting. If you find your water not hot enough, or you too often run out of hot water, move the temp selector up to the next higher setting.

PB pipe, fittings. Polybutylene is an exotic high temperature thermoplastic that makes possible flexible hot and cold water tubing. Flexibility is such that pipe from coils may be installed in long pipe runs free of joints, elbows, etc. Polybutylene pipe comes in 25-foot and 100-foot coils. Expansion of PB piping is absorbed by flexing. No noise is generated by its movement.

THE GENOGRIP™ ASSEMBLY
Shown on an angle stop

1. Squarely cut Poly Riser™ to length with jackknife allowing for full entrance and seating into Genogrip™ fitting.

2. Loosen nut on Genogrip™ fitting and stab Poly Riser™ tube fully into fitting to seated position.

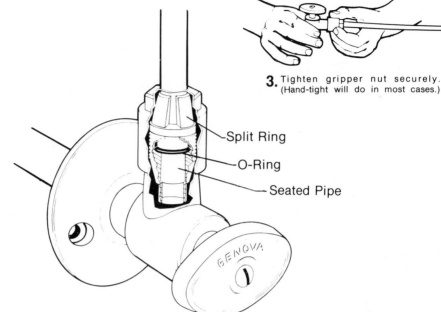

3. Tighten gripper nut securely. (Hand-tight will do in most cases.)

Split Ring

O-Ring

Seated Pipe

The biggest advantage of polybutylene pipe is its flexibility. You simply thread it through walls like an electrician "fishes" electrical cables. This feature makes PB great for remodeling work where you have no access to the insides of walls, floors and ceilings.

Polybutylene pipe is served by Genogrip™ fittings. The Genogrip™ fitting performs two functions at once: sealing off water and mechanically holding the pipe against pullout and blowout.

An elastomeric O-ring handles the water-sealing chores nicely.

To hold the pipe in place mechanically, Genova has developed a split grab-ring made of Noryl™, General Electric's trade name for polyphenylene oxide. It's a rare springy plastic material. The PB pipe inserts through it and through the neoprene O-ring to bottom out on a shoulder inside the Genogrip™ fitting. A shoulder prevents overinsertion.

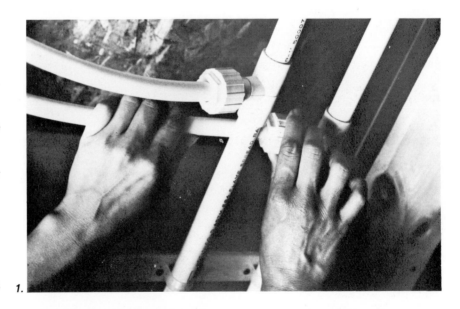

1.

1. You cannot find an easier way to install house water supply plumbing than with flexible polybutylene pipe. It can be threaded through holes in walls, floors and ceilings, wherever it needs to go.

When the fitting's nut is tightened, a cone-shaped inner surface on the nut puts the squeeze on a similarly cone-shaped outer surface of the grab-ring. A ridge inside the grab-ring digs into the PB, creating a slight groove. Ridge in groove, the PB pipe is locked in.

It cannot be pulled out by hand, nor blown out by water pressure. The resulting connection is watertight, tested to withstand 11.2 years of 200 psi at 180° F. It meets ASTM D2846-73. Actually, the burst strength of the Genogrip™ fitting exceeds that of the pipe, well over 500 psi on the hot water side, more than that on the cold water side.

A small CPVC retainer inserted in the assembly holds the O-ring in place as well as takes grab-ring thrust. The fitting may be disassembled and reconnected as often as needed. You cannot overtighten the handnut. It's designed to bottom out first.

The CPVC bodied angle and straight stops incorporating the Genogrip™ fitting solvent weld directly into a ½-inch CPVC water supply or adapt to other pipe types.

To make a Genogrip™ connection to PB, all you do is cut off the end of the PB pipe squarely with a knife--the only tool used. Make it the right length to reach, plus 1½ inches or so to enter the fitting. Then, stab it fully into the connector. Hand-tighten the nut securely and you've done it. It's a neat plug-in plumbing connection.

Genogrip™ adapters come in ⅜-, ½- and ¾-inch sizes to let you use polybutylene pipe throughout your house. They come as straight adapters (two types), angle adapters, angle stops and, what are called, stackable tees. These unique ½-inch CPVC tees branch to ⅜-inch PB and may be used for creating plumbing manifolds of CPVC to feed ⅜-inch O.D. PB tubing. All adapt to the whole range of CPVC fittings and from

these to sweat copper or threaded steel pipes and fittings. Thus, there's nothing you cannot do with a polybutylene water supply system, new or add-on. PB pipe and fittings may be buried in the ground without protection of any kind, or run between walls.

Genova also makes ⅜-inch PB pipe in the form of ready-to-use riser tubes. Called Poly Risers™, these are the hottest thing going for use with Genogrip™ fittings in hooking up water supply fixtures. The connection will take 800 psi without failure.

Poly Risers™ come two ways: bullet-nosed for connecting sinks, lavatories, and flange-ended for connecting toilets. They're flexible yet virtually impossible to kink. Poly Risers™ make a direct replacement for the old-style ⅜-inch flexible copper risers, too.

Both kinds are sold in 12- and 20-inch lengths; the lavatory type also comes in 36-inch lengths.

One caution: the Genogrip™ connection, when used on a regular chromed brass riser, needs the substitution of a serrated metal grab-ring in place of the Noryl™ one. A metal ring comes in the package. But if you're connecting a PB riser, throw it away, because the metal may cut the flexible PB tube causing a leak. Use metal with metal; Noryl™ with PB.

Genogrip™ is the easiest, fastest method for joining a plumbing fixture and its water supply, yet it's not limited to that.

2.

3.

4.

1. Genova has the best system going for installing fixture water supplies. Hot and cold water fixture shutoff valves solvent weld to CPVC stubs coming through the wall. Note the torque escutcheons.

2. With pipe end and fitting socket cemented, the Genova (Part No. 530651) ½" x ⅜" angle stop slips over the stub. Valves off, the water can be turned on before installing the fixture.

3. Genova ⅜" Poly Riser™ tube is stabbed into the valve with the handnut loosened. Then the handnut is tightened snugly. Hex head is not for tightening, but for loosening later if you can't do it by hand.

4. A floor supply to a fixture is handled similarly to a wall supply. The (Part No. 530101) CPVC/PB adapter or (Part No. 530301) straight stop is solvent welded to the stub and a flexible Poly Riser™ used to supply the faucet.

1.

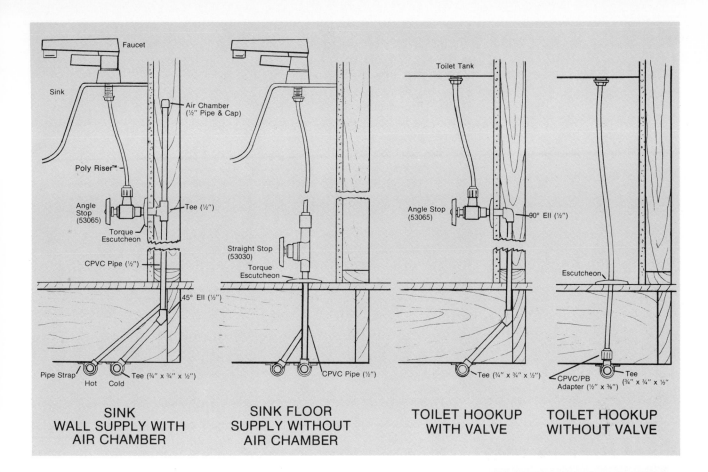

SINK WALL SUPPLY WITH AIR CHAMBER

SINK FLOOR SUPPLY WITHOUT AIR CHAMBER

TOILET HOOKUP WITH VALVE

TOILET HOOKUP WITHOUT VALVE

Which to use? CPVC may be used for any water supply purpose inside the house. So may PB. PB also may be laid below ground in a trench leading into the house from a well or the city water main.

In actual practice, here's logical reasoning on which pipe type to use. Pipe sizes for a good working installation are given, too.

Bring water into the house with ¾-inch or 1-inch polybutylene. Carry it around to fixture branches, water softener, water heater, outdoor sprinkler system and near outdoor hose bibb branches with ¾-inch CPVC pipe and fittings. Being rigid, CPVC makes a neat appearing installation.

From the house mains--hot and cold water--branch to the kitchen, sink, bathroom, laundry and hose bibbs with either ½-inch CPVC or PB pipe. PB branches to the lavatory, toilet and dishwasher may be with ⅜-inch pipe. Use CPVC for a neat appearing rigid installation, PB for the easiest

installing flexible one.

In any case, switch to PB beneath each sink and lavatory extending from fixture shutoff to faucet tailpiece with a ⅜-inch Poly Riser™. This connects to most faucets with a ⅜-inch fixture flange nut, adapts to others.

For remodeling work where the house framing isn't exposed, go PB. It is the ONLY commercially available pipe for hot and cold water that can be snaked through holes in the framing. Other flexible pipes cannot be used inside the house to carry hot water. PB pipe cost a bit more, but the work it saves more than makes up for that. Labor, yours or the plumber's, is the critical item in plumbing today.

Using PB pipe also eliminates many fittings, which saves on cost. A single run of it goes around corners that, in another pipe material, would require careful measurement and cutting, plus the use of a fitting.

BENDING OF PB PIPE

Size	Min. Bending Radius
3/8"	2"
1/2"	4"
3/4"	6"

FLOW THROUGH 3/8" PB
(gallons per minute @ 50 psi house pressure)

Length (ft.)	Flow
2	6.8
3	5.6
4	4.9
5	4.3
6	3.8
7	3.6
8	3.4
9	3.3
10	3.2

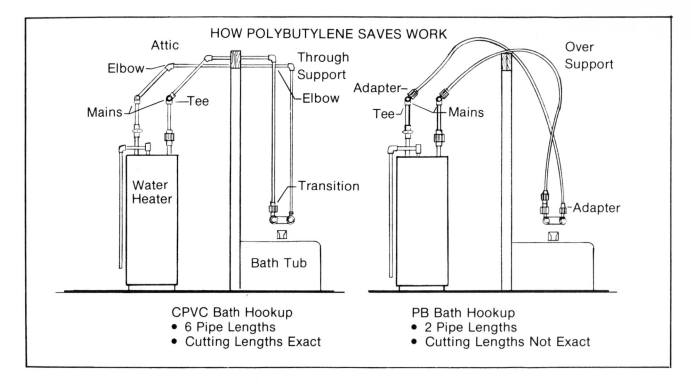

HOW POLYBUTYLENE SAVES WORK

CPVC Bath Hookup
• 6 Pipe Lengths
• Cutting Lengths Exact

PB Bath Hookup
• 2 Pipe Lengths
• Cutting Lengths Not Exact

Another way to go from house mains to fixtures is with the unique Genova-developed plumbing manifold system. You build it yourself from standard Genogrip™ and other fittings. For how to do it, see the special chapter beginning on page 30.

Other interesting fittings. The *500 Series* of Genova CPVC/PB pipes and fittings, as described in the latest catalog, is an education in water supply plumbing. Ask your dealer to look at a copy, or get one for yourself. Each fitting is explained--what it's used for, what it fits.

WHAT "STREET" MEANS

In the Genova catalog you'll run into the word *street*. Rather than the road in front of your house, *street* in this sense means pipe-sized, not fitting-sized. A street fitting has one end that slips INTO another fitting socket, like a pipe does. A 90° street elbow is used to change direction from a fitting socket. If you use a regular elbow for this, you have to prepare a short stub of pipe to link the two fittings.

More than this, Genova has made its ¾-inch CPVC street fittings do double duty as ¾ x ½

inch reducers if desired. The regular socket fits over a ¾-inch pipe. The street end fits either into a ¾-inch fitting socket or it fits over the end of a ½-inch pipe.

Other Genogrip™ adapters. Another useful fitting created by the Genova folks is the Genogrip™ universal adapter. This lets you join CPVC fittings to copper tubing without sweat soldering. It's a push-on-and-tighten operation, done in seconds without tools. It beats soldering all ways. The universal adapter also will connect to CPVC pipe on one end without solvent welding.

The universal adapter comes in ½- or ¾-inch. It works much like a Genogrip™ CPVC/PB adapter, but with a serrated grab-ring in place of the Noryl™ one. Although the universal adapter will work initially on PB pipe, it's not recommended because of the cutting metal grab-ring.

The universal adapter can be used in conjunction with CPVC fittings for an unlimited range of fittings that will adapt copper tubing and CPVC mechanically.

Line Stops. Other Genova firsts in plumbing are Part No. 530151 and Part No. 530161, line stops.

Designed to be ½-inch or ¾-inch street, they employ the globe-valve principle. However, their inner design permits fantastic flow rates far in excess of standard ½-inch globe-type valves.

The Genova line stop fits a ½-inch line direct. The addition of two ¾-inch couplings turns it into a ¾-inch valve to serve as a main house shutoff valve.

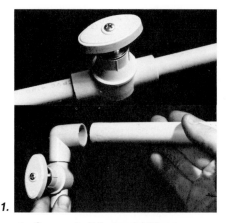

1.

1. Genova's ¾" street fittings are designed to see duty either as ½" or ¾". At top, the CPVC (Part No. 530151) line stop acts as a standard ½" valve. At bottom, with a ¾" elbow, it becomes a ¾" valve.

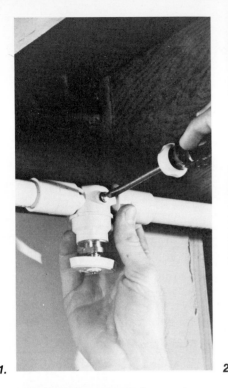

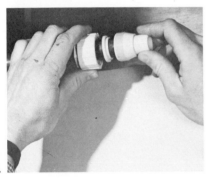

1.

2.

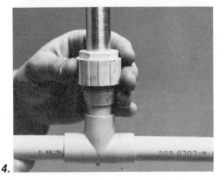

3.

4.

AUTHOR'S FLOW TESTS on Genova ¾" x ½" Line Stop (@ 50 psi)	
Tested	Flow (gpm)
Line Stop	7.36
½" Angle Stop	6.38
¾" Globe Valve	6.98
¾" Copper Pipe	7.96

1. Genova's (Part No. 530161) ¾" x ½" line stop comes with a waste opening, making it a stop-and-waste valve for draining plumbing before leaving a house unheated during below-freezing weather.

2. Genova's unique line stops feature patented full-flow design. Water enters from left and bends up to globe valve at full bore. Cross-sectional area from valve to outlet (at right) exceeds that of pipe.

3. Innovative Genogrip™ universal adapter locks onto copper tubing or CPVC pipe by hand-tightening. Here, shown taken apart, it clamps a serrated metal grab-ring and rubber O-ring around pipe.

4. When the handnut is tightened, fitting locks onto the pipe. The end is street CPVC, that is, it slips into a CPVC fitting. A universal adapter may be removed whenever desired. In actual use, the universal adapter is not taken apart but merely pushed onto the pipe and tightened. Then it can be solvent welded to any CPVC fitting to join copper tubing and CPVC pipe without soldering.

Here's the Manifold System

Whether you are adding a bathroom or plumbing a whole house with bath, consider using a plumbing manifold. It's a Genova idea that you can make at home. There's no easier, better way to handle a bathroom water supply.

The plumbing manifold's working parts mount inside a small wooden enclosure. The basis of the manifold is the Genova (Part No. 530051) stackable tee. The manifold itself fits inside a bathroom wall. It contains two or more valves controlling water to the bathroom fixtures. These are reached through a hinged access door. Water from the house hot and cold mains enters the manifold's inlet side via two ½-inch polybutylene tubes. These adapt to whatever kind of pipes your house has and push into the CPVC/PB Genogrip™ adapters in the manifold.

Leading to the toilet, lavatory and tub/shower, other PB tubes supply the bathroom fixtures with hot and cold water. These, too, push into Genogrip™ adapters. At the fixture end, they attach either with fixture flange nuts (jam nuts) or adapters.

1. A plumbing manifold bathroom--the manifold is located to the lower left of the toilet tank--works differently from a standard bath. All water supplies route through the manifold where valves control flow to the fixtures.

The manifold itself is assembled of Genova *500 Series* fittings as shown in the accompanying shopping list.

We illustrate two kinds of plumbing manifolds. Genova Board Chairman, R. F. Williams, prefers the two-valve version. In an emergency, he points out, all water to the bathroom group could be turned off quickly even without knowing which valve controls which fixture. I lean toward the five-valve version for its more complete water control. It's a hybrid version made without using any stackable tees. Of course you may build either version or innovate your own design.

Tube-sizing. Each manifold is really two separate ones. One carries hot water, the other cold. Although the two share the manifold enclosure, they are not interconnected. The hot water side contains two supply outlets. One leads to the lavatory, the other to the tub/shower. The cold water side contains three supply outlets. One leads to the lavatory, one to the tub/shower and the third to the toilet.

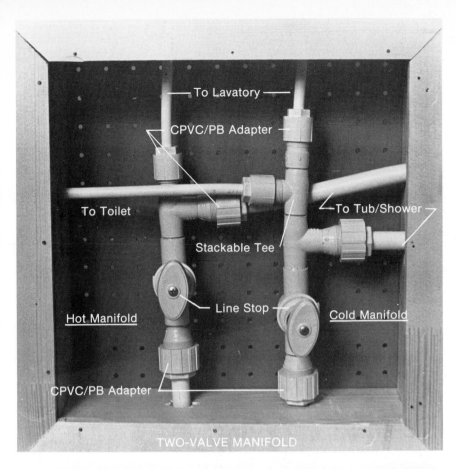

To Lavatory

CPVC/PB Adapter

To Toilet

Stackable Tee

To Tub/Shower

Hot Manifold

Line Stop

Cold Manifold

CPVC/PB Adapter

TWO-VALVE MANIFOLD

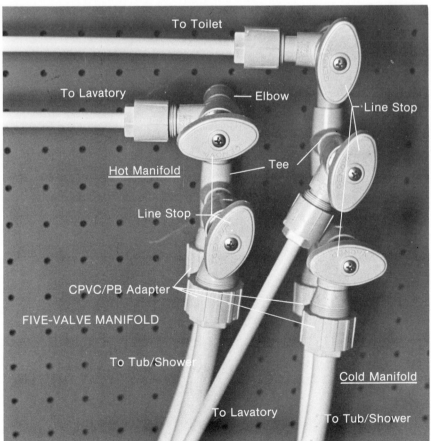

To Toilet

To Lavatory

Elbow

Line Stop

Hot Manifold

Tee

Line Stop

CPVC/PB Adapter

FIVE-VALVE MANIFOLD

Cold Manifold

To Tub/Shower

To Lavatory

To Tub/Shower

Outlet tube sizes should be as shown in the table to provide the required water flow to each fixture. A lavatory and shower-only need three gallons a minute supplied to both hot and cold sides. That's all the flow their faucets can handle. A toilet needs about the same flow of cold water only. If the toilet receives a little less flow, it can get by. In that case the flush tank would merely take a bit longer to refill after each flush. A bathtub or shower with bath needs five gallons a minute flow, so does a kitchen sink. The flow rates shown in the table are measured at 50 psi house water pressure. Most city water pressure runs from 50 to 80 psi. As you can see, by keeping your ⅜-inch tube runs short you could supply all bath fixtures with ⅜-inch PB.

Merely by changing the manifold's design slightly and adding two ½-inch outlets at the top, it can also serve a nearby kitchen sink or other fixture requiring ½-inch tubes. These additional outlets give it flow-through design. The added tubes also could serve another plumbing manifold in another bathroom. Don't, however, connect more than two manifolds in a series unless you make the main supply manifolds of ¾-inch pipe and fittings.

Manifold-building. Make up your plumbing manifold ahead of time. That's the best way, I decided, after assembling one on-site. Prebuilding is the way Genova intended.

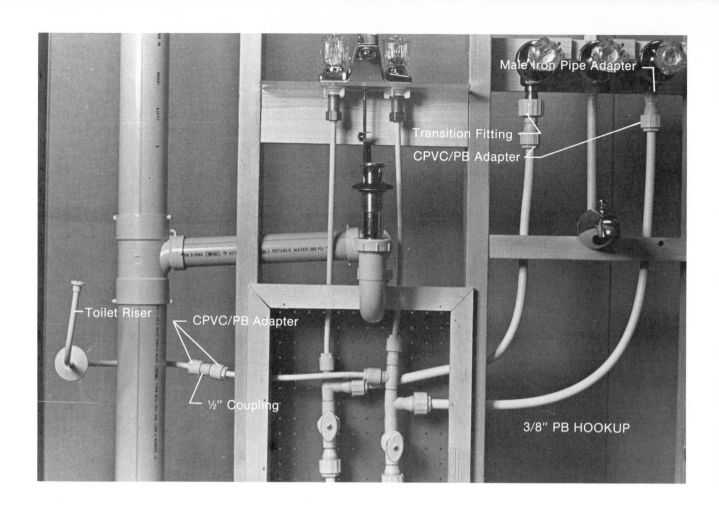

Male Iron Pipe Adapter

Transition Fitting

CPVC/PB Adapter

Toilet Riser

CPVC/PB Adapter

½" Coupling

3/8" PB HOOKUP

Tube Sizes to Fixtures			
Fixture	To 4' Run	To 10' Run	Over 10' Run
Lavatory and toilet	3/8"	3/8"	3/8"*
Shower alone	3/8"	3/8"	1/2"
Tub/shower or kitchen sink	3/8"	1/2"	1/2"
*reduced flow			

Make the enclosure of scrap wood 3½ inches deep. This fits flush into a standard 2 x 4-inch stud wall. The five-valve version needs to be deeper. Glue-nail a 1½-inch wood frame onto the 4-inch deep box. Make it of 1½" x 1½" members. Make the manifold enclosure 10 inches wide and 12½ inches high on the inside. A manifold with top outlets and flow-through design should be two inches taller than shown. The manifold back can be ¼-inch hardboard or plywood.

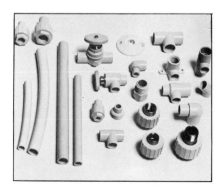

Plumbing Manifold Shopping List

Genova Pt. No.	Qty.	Description

TWO-VALVE VERSION

530051	3	½" CPVC x ⅜" PB Stackable Tees
530151	2	¾"/½" Line Stops
530751	4	½" CPVC/PB Genogrip™ Adapters
(Add for flow-through design)		
51405	2	½" CPVC Tees
530151	2	¾"/½" Line Stops
530751	2	½" CPVC/PB Genogrip™ Adapters

FIVE-VALVE VERSION

530651	3	½" CPVC x ⅜" PB Angle Stops
530661	2	½" Angle Stops
530751	4	½" CPVC/PB Genogrip™ Adapters
51405	3	½" Tees
52905	2	½" 90° CPVC Street Elbows
(Add for flow-through design)		
51405	2	½" CPVC Tees
530751	2	½" CPVC/PB Genogrip™ Adapters
530151	2	¾"/½" Line Stops
52905	2*	½" CPVC 90° Street Elbows *optional (not needed)

PIPING, HOOKUP, ETC. (for ½" tub/shower supply)

14010	1	¼ Pint Novaclean™ Primer (No. 1)
14110	1	¼ Pint Novaweld C™ Solvent (No. 2)
53421	1	½" x 100' PB Pipe
50005	1	½" x 10' CPVC Pipe
530881	1 pr.	⅜" x 36" PB Lavatory Riser Tubes
530821	1	⅜" x 20" PB Toilet Riser Tubes
530751	6	½" CPVC/PB Genogrip™ Adapters (two adapters for ½" sweat-copper tub/shower valve.)
51471	2	¾" x ¾" x ½" CPVC Reducing Tees
530851	4	¾" CPVC/SWT Cpr.Genogrip™Adapters (for sweat-copper mains)
530401	4	¾" CPVC/FIP Transition Unions (for steel mains)
530451	2	¾" CPVC/MIP Transition Unions (for ½" threaded tub/shower valve)
50105	2	½" CPVC Couplings
50405	1	½" CPVC/MIP Male Adapter (for shower riser from threaded tub/shower valve. Substitute additional 530751 for sweat-copper tub/shower valve.)
530551	1	½" CPVC Wing Elbow
52105	1	Bag ½" CPVC/PB Tubing Straps
530121	3	⅜" CPVC Escutcheons

Assemble the hot and cold CPVC manifolds, solvent welding the parts in proper position. Where ½-inch nipples are needed to join two fitting sockets, make them of 1½-inch lengths of ½-inch CPVC tube. If desired, the hot and cold manifolds may be strapped to the back with blocking behind to keep the handnuts from resting on the backing.

Locate your manifold conveniently, yet close enough to the fixtures to keep the tube runs within reason. Before you fasten it in place with nails or screws, drill holes in the manifold top, bottom and sides as needed. Align them with all inlet and outlet adapters. Drill ½-inch holes for ⅜-inch tubes and ¾-inch holes for ½-inch tubes. Drill matching holes in the house framing for routing of all tubes. These may be larger.

pipe (not shown in shopping list). Solvent weld a (Part No. 530751) ½-inch CPVC/PB Genogrip™ adapter directly into the ½-inch tee branch. From there you go clear to the manifold using easy-working, flexible ½-inch PB tube.

You can adapt to sweat-copper tubing using the same setup, but in place of the transition unions use (Part No. 530851) ¾-inch Genova Genogrip™ adapters having stainless steel grab-rings. No sweat soldering is needed. These push onto the ends of the cut-off copper tubes and tighten up leak-free. The ¾-inch reducing tee solvent welds over the street ends of the universal adapters.

The ½-inch PB feed tubes stab into their adapters at the bottom of the manifold. (If your house is plumbed from the attic, the feed end would be at the

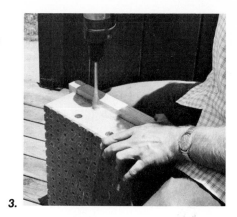

3.

4.

Manifold hookup. It's best to install your manifold before the finished wall material goes on. It can be done afterward, but you'll have to fish the tubes through. They're flexible, so this is possible.

Install the water feed tubes to the manifold first. You can adapt to threaded pipe house mains by cutting out a section and re-threading both cutoff ends. Then screw on ¾-inch Genova (Part No. 530401) CPVC/FIP (female-threaded) transition unions. These solvent weld to (Part No. 51471) ¾ x ¾ x ½-inch CPVC reducing tees using short ¾-inch nipples cut from CPVC

top of the manifold.)

For easy insertion chamfer all around the ends of the ½-inch PB tubes at a 45-degree angle using sandpaper or a file. Put a little petroleum jelly on the adapters' O-rings. Then stab in fully and hand-tighten the nuts. If you like, you may tighten ½-inch and larger Genogrip™ hand-nuts with water-pump pliers. Don't go overboard on tightness, though. I found firm hand-tightening more than adequate.

Next run the supply tubes to their fixtures and connect them in the normal manner (see the chapter on connecting fixtures beginning on page 48).

1.

2.

1. Preassemble the hot and cold manifolds before solvent welding to check for fit inside enclosure. Next, solvent weld, carefully aligning each joint.

2. Mark enclosure for feed and supply tube holes.

3. Drill ¾" holes for ½" tubes and ½" holes for ⅜" tubes.

4. Also drill holes for the feed and supply tubes through wall and floor framing. Make them ¼" larger than holes in enclosure.

2.

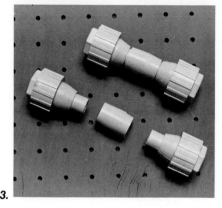

3.

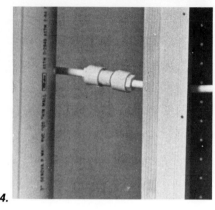

1.

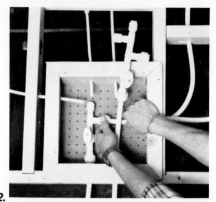

4.

*FOR CLARITY THESE PHOTO-
GRAPHS WERE TAKEN OF A
SIMULATED PLUMBING
SYSTEM INSTALLATION.*

*1. Cut into the house hot and
cold water mains and adapt them
for the ½″ PB feeder runs to the
manifold with a tee or a straight
connection. Here, a copper tee
was used to polybutylene. This
consists of a ½″ transition fitting
and a ½″ CPVC/PB Genogrip™
adapter.*

*2. It is not necessary to
disassemble the Genogrip™
adapters to attach the polybutylene tubes. Simply stab the
tubes into the adapters and
hand-tighten the nuts. Connect
the ½″ tubes first, then the
⅜″ ones.*

*3. PB couplings can be made from
short pieces of PB tubing. They
consist of two CPVC/PB Geno-
grip™ adapters joined by a CPVC
coupling.*

*4. Two Poly Risers™ are joined
with Genogrip™ adapters to
extend a toilet riser tube.*

If you keep your ⅜-inch lavatory and toilet supply runs
less than 36 and 20 inches,
respectively, you can use Genova
ready-made Poly Riser™ tubes.
This eases the job. Otherwise,
buy bulk ⅜-inch PB tubing and
cut it to length. Soft rubber
ferrules, friction rings and
fixture nuts will make plain-
ended connections watertight at
at the fixtures. Using riser
tubes, be sure to install the
fixture nuts over the tubes before fishing the risers through
the wall toward the manifold
or connecting to the manifold.
Otherwise, you'll have to take
the risers out again to put on
the nuts.

Handling details. Supply tubes
can be fastened to cross-
pieces behind the wall for
support. Those for lavatories
should come out of the wall 22
inches above the floor and eight
inches apart on centers. For
the toilet, bring the tube out of
the wall six inches above the
floor and eight inches to the
left of the toilet's centerline.
All tubes should exit the wall
at right angles so their escutcheons will fit squarely.

Raw wall exit openings may be
hidden using split escutcheons.
You can make them from regular
Genova ⅜-inch escutcheons by
slitting with a sharp knife. Put a
little wallboard adhesive on the
back of each escutcheon and it
will be held tightly to the wall.

Supply tubes push in and are
hand-tightened at the manifold.
Then you're ready to test your
job for leaks.

Support runs of PB as
described on page 23. See
that the PB tubes aren't
bent sharper than they're supposed to be (see page 27). Be sure
to protect tubing runs from nails
using steel straps as necessary.

Make an access door for your
manifold using ⅛-inch plywood.
Identify the valves with label
tape for centralized control of the
bathroom water supply.

You can plumb all the way to
the shower with vinyl. A plain
(Part No. 50405) ½-inch male
CPVC adapter may be used
between the shower valve and
its ½-inch CPVC riser to the
shower arm. A transition union
is not needed there. This is
because water pressure at that
point is minimal. Put a little
silicone sealant on all vinyl
threads before making them up.

The fixture drain-waste-vent
system is built using Genova PVC
pipes and fittings as described
in another chapter. Whether you
use a water supply manifold or
not has no effect on its
construction.

The Vinyl Drain Waste & Vent System

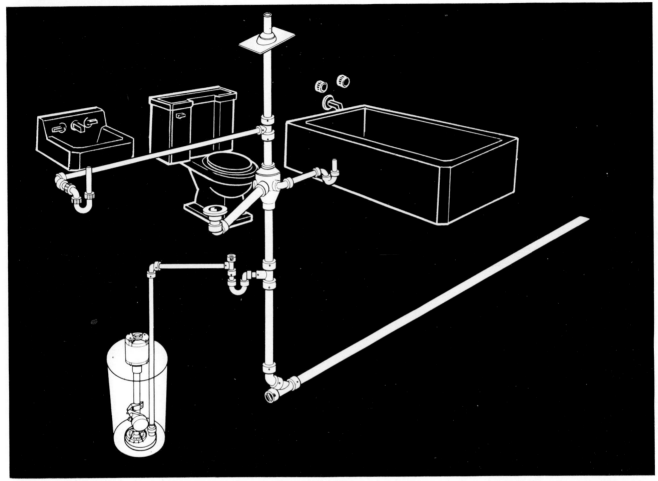

Your house drain-waste-vent system carries liquids and solids away from the fixtures and out of the house. At this job, vinyl excels. Vinyl piping materials have such terrific chemical resistance and resistance to corrosion that they're used in chemical plants to convey concentrated acids and strong alkaline solutions. These chemicals would quickly destroy metal piping.

With Genova PVC-DWV materials, you can get a chemical-plant-quality plumbing system for your own house.

The best part is that PVC installs so simply. As with CPVC piping, the joints between pipes and fittings are made by simple solvent welding. Lightweight PVC is easy to handle. For example, a 10-foot length of 2-inch PVC-DWV pipe weighs only six pounds. It takes the strain out of installing pipes in hard-to-reach places.

What's more, hammer blows that would hopelessly dent copper pipe, merely glance harmlessly off Genova rigid vinyl pipe. Rough handling, backfilling, traffic loads, temperature changes, vibration--all hazards that make metallic piping systems unusable--are no problem with Genova's superior vinyl.

Genova PVC-DWV pipe and fittings conform to ASTM D2665 and ASTM D2949. They're unaffected by strong acids, alkalies, salt solutions, alcohols, and many other chemicals. Genova rigid vinyl possesses outstanding weathering characteristics. Even in direct sunlight, there's no need to provide protection, either before or after installation. PVC is resistant to fungi, bacterial action, and adverse soil conditions. Like CPVC pipe, PVC permits no possibility of electrolytic action to destroy the system.

Cleaners okay. The unwettable mirror-smooth interior passages of PVC pipe offer less resistance to flow with resulting higher through-put both initially and after years of service. Surfaces stay smooth, DWV lines stay open. They seldom, if ever, need cleaning. If drain cleaning ever IS required, you can pour chemical cleaners down your PVC drains with full assurance that the pipes are completely impervious to them. Makers of ordinary "plastic" plumbing products cannot match this.

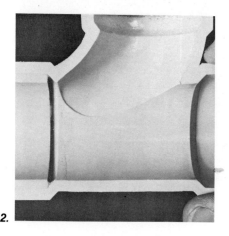

1.

2.

A PVC pipe system will take all the hot drain water you could want to put down it.

PVC pipes will not support combustion, so fire cannot travel along them. This accounts for the special approval of PVC piping by so many plumbing codes nationwide. Genova vinyl products have been awarded a flame-spread rating of 10 in accordance with ASTM procedure E-84. (That's good!)

Genova DWV pipes and fittings come in five diameters: 6-inch, 4-inch, 3-inch, 2-inch and 1½-inch. It's doubtful that

you'll ever need the 6-inch size. Genova PVC pipe offers you an economical yet superior solution to your DWV home plumbing project.

IN-WALL

Genova DWV systems are made in two lines of pipe and fittings. One is called Schedule 40 DWV, and the other, Schedule 30 In-Wall. Unique Schedule 30 was developed by Genova specifically for home handyman plumbing. Its somewhat thinner walls than standard Schedule 40 earn it the 30 designation. The whole idea behind Genova In-Wall is that it will fit a 2 x 4-inch stud wall. A 3-inch In-Wall stack, with fittings, fits inside a standard house wall, yet it has the same performance as a larger-on-the-outside 3-inch Schedule 40 stack, which will not fit inside a stud wall.

This means that, using an In-Wall system, you needn't fur out house walls to fit a plumbing stack into them. Only Genova offers Schedule 30.

Genova In-Wall pipe and fittings come only in 3-inch. The reason for the single size is almost obvious. A 4-inch Schedule 30, if available, wouldn't fit into a stud wall anyway. And the smaller sizes of Schedule 40, 2- and 1½-inch, already fit into a wall. Standard 3-inch Schedule 40 pipe will not fit 3-inch Schedule 30 fittings, so don't try to mix the two.

In-Wall pipe and fittings are sold as *600 Series* in the Genova catalog.

Because Genova In-Wall pipe and fittings go into standard stud walls without compromising performance, they've become the accepted standard in many areas of the United States.

We recommend using In-Wall. Order all your 3-inch pipes and fittings of it. For the smaller sizes simply order standard Schedule 40. These fit Schedule 30 In-Wall fittings direct. No adapters are needed. For example, a 3 x 3 x 1½-inch In-Wall tee fits Schedule 30 pipe at its 3-inch sockets and

Schedule 40 pipe at its 1½-inch branch socket.

When you must use 3-inch Schedule 40 DWV pipes in a 2 x 4 stud wall, you'll have to fur the wall out about an inch to accommodate them. Schedule 40 pipes and fittings are listed as the *700 Series* in Genova's catalog.

To make a 3-inch Schedule 40 pipe, join a 3-inch Schedule 30 In-Wall pipe or fitting. This requires an adapter. My advice, avoid Schedule 40 in the 3-inch size.

Here's a recap for ordering:
All 3-inch--order Schedule 30 In-Wall *600 Series* pipe and fittings.

Any other size fitting that does not include any 3-inch, plus 1½- and 2-inch pipe-- order Schedule 40 *700 Series*. No adapters are needed between the two, unless you go to a 4-inch size.

1. The solvent resistance of PVC pipe is much greater than that of ordinary ABS plastic pipe. Both were doped with PVC, solvent cement, then scratched. ABS scratched much more deeply.

2. Solvent welding makes a PVC pipe and its fitting one. Under extreme laboratory test pressures, the pipe fails before the joint. (Note the inside contours of a drainage tee.)

1.

1. Genova Schedule 30 DWV
In-Wall pipe and fitting (left)
will just fit inside a standard 2 x 4
stud wall. The Schedule 40 fitting
(right) will not. Both inside diameters are about the same.

2. The difference between
Schedule 40 (right) and Genova
Schedule 30 In-Wall is the wall
thickness of pipes and fittings.
Because In-Wall is so easy to use,
it is accepted by many codes.

3. Closeup shows the markings
that identify a Genova PVC In-Wall
vinyl fitting for DWV use and
indicate its wide acceptance.
It is Part No. 60630. "Thin-Wall"
was an earlier name for Genova
In-Wall.

4. If you use Schedule 40 pipe and
run a 3-inch vent stack through
the wall behind the toilet, fur
out the standard 2 x 4 stud wall
almost an inch with wood strips
nailed to the studs.

2.

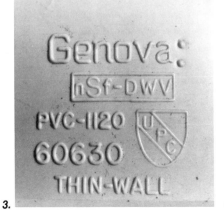

3.

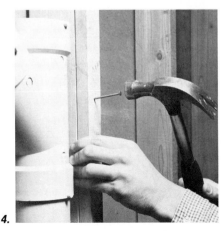

4.

FACTS ON FITTINGS

There's a whole story to tell on buying DWV pipe and fittings. It's summed up: get everything from one manufacturer!

Here's why. Present ASTM standards for drain-waste-vent pipe and fittings represent the consensus of pipe and fitting manufacturers' thoughts on the dimensions they can economically hold on a mass production basis. Nothing wrong with that. However, those dimensions and the tolerances allowed in them were based on the fact that most manufacturers made pipe only, or fittings only, but not both as Genova does.

Take an example, a 3-inch size, say, and see how the standards actually work out.

From the table of ASTM pipe dimensions and tolerances note that an outside diameter tolerance of 0.008 of an inch either way is allowed on 3-inch pipe. That's a total of 0.016 of an inch from largest to smallest pipe permitted. In addition, an out-of-round of up to 0.015 is allowed. Note, too, that the pipe's wall thickness may not be less than 0.216 of an inch, but it can be quite a bit thicker.

Suppose that Joe Blow Pipe Making Company makes a truckload of his pipes for your local cut-rate distributor. Joe is going to interpret those tolerances to his benefit. Can't blame him. To use the least materials in producing carloads of pipe, he's going to shade the outside diameter down to 3.495 inches plus 0.005 inches or minus 0.003 inch, which he can meet. Besides that he's going to skinny down the pipe's wall thickness to 0.219 inch plus or minus 0.003 inch. If Joe doesn't do these things, it could cost him 12 percent more to make the pipes. That's more than his profit, so he does this or he goes broke.

Fit: all fittings. Now, look at the ASTM fitting dimensions and tolerances table. Pete Smith's Fitting Manufacturing Company must follow these, and Pete has a whole different set of production problems. Pete knows that his fittings must fit everybody's pipe, even that made by the pipe manufacturer who has poor extrusion machinery, worse quality control and who doesn't care how much material he puts into a pipe. So, Pete Smith stays on the high side of the plus or minus 0.015-inch fitting tolerances. This way his 3-inch fitting socket will fit over all manufacturers' 3-inch pipes.

If you press a few buttons on your electronic calculator, you'll get the idea fast. A 3-inch pipe could have an outside diameter as small as 3.492 inches and still meet specs. A 3-inch fitting could have a socket entrance diameter as large as 3.535 inches and meet specs. That's a slop fit of 0.043 of an inch, half-way between 1/32 and 1/16 inch.

On top of that, if the allowable out-of-roundness in both pipe and fitting happen to fall into place out of sequence, and it easily could, this adds another whopping slop factor. Moreover, when a cheap, watery solvent cement is used to weld the joint, it's no wonder that leaks develop.

Not Genova. On the other hand, Genova doesn't work that way. The father-son Williams' team, when they went into the pipe and fittings manufacturing business, approached it as a total concept. They wanted to make house plumbing easier and more successful for the home handyman, so they threw away the industry accepted tolerances. These weren't close enough. The Williams' hold their pipes to a plus 0.003 minus zero tolerance, and they make fittings to fit their own pipe, not Joe Blow's or anyone else's. That would only end up in disaster.

Genova's fittings can be made to much closer tolerances, too. Other large fitting makers produce both PVC and ABS. ABS has a much greater shrink factor, so dual-marking fitting dies must be larger and the injection molding procedures are manipulated to stay within the broad tolerances. Genova avoids all this by making ONLY PVC pipes and fittings to fit them.

You'll notice that most solvent welding instructions tell you, "Test-fit the fitting on the pipe. If it won't go on or if it goes on loosely and falls off when inverted, you can't make a good joint with it." And, they're right.

If you use all Genova pipes and fittings, you can forget these directions. Genova materials fit every time, so don't ask your dealer whether the yellow pipe will work with the gray fitting. Just make sure that everything you get is Genova, then you know they go together. Enough said.

ASTM DWV STANDARDS
D2661 (ABS)
D2665 (PVC)

PIPE DIMENSIONS AND TOLERANCES

Nominal Size	Outside Diameter			Wall Thickness	
	Average	Tolerance	Out-of-Round	Minimum	Tolerance
3″	3.500″	±0.008″	±0.015″	0.216″	-0.000″ +0.026″

FITTING DIMENSIONS AND TOLERANCES

Nominal Size	Socket Entrance Dia.		Socket Bottom Dia.		Socket Depth	Wall Thickness (min.)
	Average	Tolerance	Average	Tolerance		
3″	3.520″	±0.015″	3.495″	±0.015″	1½″	0.219″

WORKING WITH DWV

Like CPVC water supply pipe, PVC pipes for DWV use are joined by solvent welding. The same two-step procedure is used, except that you'll need a different solvent cement. For most solvent welding at room temperature and in warm weather, use Genova Novaweld P™ cement. For low-temperature solvent welding of PVC-DWV, use Arcticweld P™.

Each solvent is especially formulated to develop after a five minute setting time at its rated temperature; 375 pounds resistance to pull-out on a 1½-inch PVC pipe. All three meet ASTM D2564-67. Can sizes come from four ounces to a quart.

The handy dauber that comes with the pint size of Novaweld P™ is the right size for welding up to 2-inch PVC pipe. For larger sizes, use a paintbrush to apply cement. Brush width should be about half the diameter of the pipe you'll be using it on. For a 3-inch joint, use a 1½-inch wide brush.

First, clean the joint with Novaclean™ using a clean, lint-free rag. Then, pour some solvent into a clean coffee can and dip the brush into it. Coat the pipe end, dip the brush again and coat the fitting socket. Liberal coats of cement ensure leak-free joints, just as with CPVC.

Tips. To get square ends, saw PVC pipes in a miter box if you have one, or sever them with a pipe cutter having a special vinyl-cutting wheel.

Clean pipe and fittings with Novaclean™. Lay the pipe on 2 x 4 blocks to prevent contamination of the cleaned surfaces.

Examine the pipe end for damage, such as deep scratches, abrasions and hairline cracks caused by heavy impacts. If necessary, cut off a damaged

SOLVENT WELDING PVC PIPE

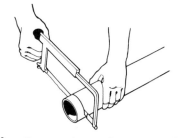

1. Cut to length squarely and allow for makeup dimension (depth of fitting socket). Use a fine-tooth saw or a pipe cutter with a special vinyl cutting wheel.

2. Remove all burrs on pipe end using sandpaper or a knife.

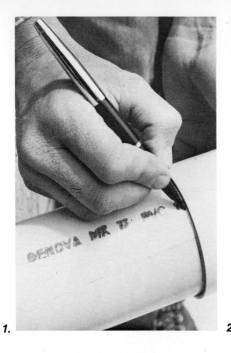

1.

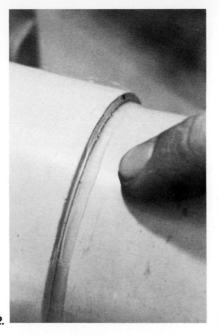

2.

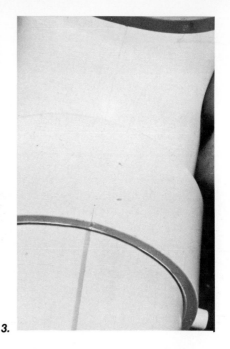

3.

end and discard it. Then use a file or coarse sandpaper to chamfer the pipe end all around at a 45-degree angle. This helps it to enter the fitting cleanly.

Do your solvent welding of DWV pipe sizes across a pair of 2 x 4's to keep the pipes and fittings aligned up off the floor. Take care not to spill solvent cements on a finished floor. Also, remember that they're flammable. Don't open the containers until you're ready to solvent weld.

Pipe alignment. All Genova PVC pipe fittings contain degree marks around their edges at 45-degree increments. The marks

help you to get each fitting properly aligned during the solvent welding process. By aligning the proper degree mark with the unique "plumbline" along the full length of every Genova PVC-DWV type pipe, you can align fittings at either end of the pipe in relation to each other. Exactly. It's a great feature, because you haven't much time to get a solvent welded fitting into alignment before it becomes immovable.

1. One good way to get a square saw cut is to slide a slip coupling over the pipe and use it to mark squarely around the pipe. Then follow by sawing the pipe to the line you made.

2. If the completed joint has a fillet of solvent around it, you used enough solvent. If there's no fillet or if it isn't continuous, use more cement on the next solvent welded joint.

3. Degree marks around the outsides of all Genova DWV fittings, together with a "plumbline" on every pipe, let you accurately align DWV fittings as you go. Marks show 45 and 90 degrees.

3. With a clean rag, wipe Novaclean™ on pipe and socket.

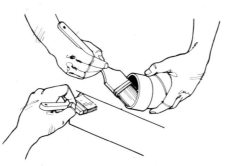

4. Follow immediately with Novaweld P™ or Novaweld All Purpose™ application. Apply Novaweld™ solvent liberally on pipe and sparingly on socket.

5. Quickly push the pipe into the socket with a slight twisting motion until it bottoms. Adjust alignment of fitting immediately, before the solvent sets up.

Allow for expansion. PVC pipe expands and contracts with changes in temperature. The normal direction changes in DWV piping account for this, but if you have an unusually long run followed by a short offset of 45 or 90 degrees, supports at the change of direction should be tightly clamped to the pipe to prevent heavy flex-loading of the fittings. If the change of direction is followed by a longer run (20 diameters or more), support the pipe loosely to allow movement.

Support horizontal runs of all PVC pipe sizes every 48 inches (every third joist). Vertical runs are rested on wood blocking at the lower end. Branching runs also help support them.

All drainage runs should slope toward the drain ¼-inch per foot. Only drainage fittings should be used for drain runs. Sharp-turn vent-type fittings may be used in vent runs. If drainage fittings such as tees or wyes are used in vent runs, install them upside down.

Threaded fittings. Special directions for assembling threaded PVC-DWV fittings call for the use of a strap wrench. While pipe wrenches tend to chew up vinyl fittings, they will work. Dry-fit the threaded fitting counting the number of turns required to make it hand-tight. Remove it. Apply Teflon™ tape or non-hardening pipe dope to the male threads and reassemble. Screw in the fitting in the same number of turns required for hand-tight without the tape or dope, then give it one-and-one-half turns additional. That's all.

Should you ever need to join your PVC-DWV system to some part of an ordinary plastic one made of ABS, you may do it by solvent welding. Use Novaweld P™ solvent cement, but be careful.

ABS plastic is much less chemically resistant than PVC. The solvent's attacking power can soften the ABS to the point where it fails. Use enough cement to make the joint, but don't be as

liberal with it as in solvent welding PVC. The saying, "You cannot use too much cement," doesn't apply to solvent welding ABS.

Fittings you'll like. Pop-Top™ closet flanges have been mentioned. They're used to join the toilet to the DWV system. Besides the flashed over opening, you'll like the patented teeth along the edge of the closet flange bolt slots. These hold toilet bolts fixed while you set the toilet bowl. They give you an extra "arm" when you need one.

Along with running vent stacks out through the roof comes the problem of weather-sealing between the stack and the roofing. Metal flashings, because of their different rates of thermal expansion, are almost impossible to seal around a vinyl or plastic pipe. Genova solved the problem with its Snap-Fit™ thermo-plastic roof flashing base and neoprene collar. The two parts snap together. Available in 1½-, 2-, 3- and 4-inch, the flashing clings tightly to the vent pipe and prevents leaking. What's more, it eliminates unsightly shingle staining caused by corroding metal flashings.

Snap-Fit™ collars also may be used singly as rain collars over old leaking metal flashings. Bases and collars are sold either assembled or separate.

A fitting that eases. Another product you'll appreciate is the Genova special waste and vent fitting. It takes the place of a sanitary tee under the floor behind the toilet. Made in 3-inch Schedule 30 and 3- and 4-inch Schedule 40, it accepts the toilet's vent stack and drain line at full bore. A pair of reduced side tappings let 2- or 1½-inch lavatory or tub-shower waste lines be connected. If you don't need the side tappings, solvent weld plugs are available to close them.

At the lower end of the special waste and vent fitting, either of two types of bottom caps may be solvent welded in place. Both accept the main stack full bore. One also has a 1½-inch tapping for an additional drain or vent run.

The special waste and vent fitting is available in either single or double configuration for use with one or two toilets. Two toilet drainage lines enter the double configuration fitting

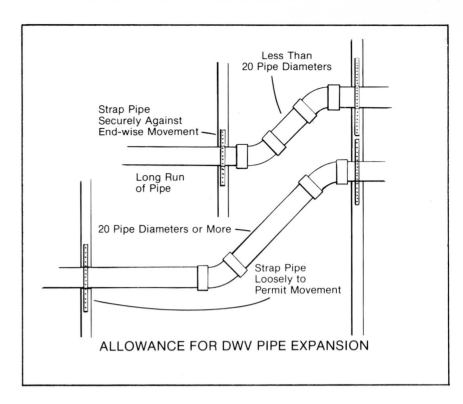

Less Than 20 Pipe Diameters

Strap Pipe Securely Against End-wise Movement

Long Run of Pipe

20 Pipe Diameters or More

Strap Pipe Loosely to Permit Movement

ALLOWANCE FOR DWV PIPE EXPANSION

1.

3.

4.

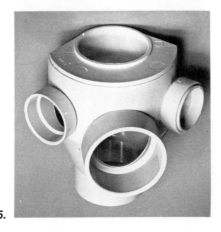

2.

1. *Two piece, no maintenance Genova Snap-Fit™ flashing is designed for use with vinyl pipe as well as all other plumbing pipes. Base fits underneath roofing, cap slides down over vent stack. They snap together for a rain-tight fit.*

2. *Genova Pop-Top™ closet flange for toilet installation contains a flashed over opening to keep the DWV system clean. When you're ready to install the toilet, simply tap it out with a hammer.*

3. *Backwater valve by Genova keeps flood water in a low sewer from entering your basement. Easy-off access cover allows cleanout of the one-way built-in flapper valve inside the body.*

4. *Genova offers a variety of reducing couplings and bushings to enable you to change pipe sizes easily. They just solvent weld in!*

5. *Special Waste and Vent Fitting. (Single Configuration)*

back-to-back. This fitting simplifies the early steps in building a successful DWV system.

If you ever need to join a Genova PVC drain-waste-vent pipe to an existing cast iron pipe, get a Genova hub adapter. Its special vinyl formulation permits pouring of molten lead to adapt directly to a cast iron hub with an old-style lead-and-oakum joint.

5.

On the other hand, you'll probably prefer not to use hot lead since there is an easier way. Use Genova's special plastic lead compound, filling the hub joint with it. When it sets, the joint is sealed against leakage. It's much easier than working with lead and oakum. Directions are on the can.

Drains. Genova features a complete line of roof drains, floor drains and shower drains. All solvent weld directly to PVC pipe without costly transitions to metal drains.

Genova's Toe-Saver™ floor plug fits flush with the floor to seal a floor level cleanout opening without parts that stick up to trip someone. Use it in traffic areas, such as a basement floor. The Toe Saver™ comes in 3- and 4-inch.

Kits. To save you the trouble of ordering materials separately, Genova has developed the Bath Pak. It has all the fittings you normally need for a bathroom DWV installation. The Bath Pak, shown on page 47, is furnished complete with roof flashing, cement and easy-to-follow instructions.

Genova's PVC-DWV systems outlast cast iron and other back-breaking materials. They not only cost less, you can put them in yourself. A paintbrush and handsaw make you the best plumber on the block, and you can get any of the do-it-yourself products at your local hardware or home center.

1.

2.

1. Floor Drain

2. Roof Drain

3. Nothing beats Genova's polypropylene Twist-Lok™ cleanout plug. To install it in any Genova DWV fitting, just insert the plug into the same-sized fitting socket all the way. Genova DWV fittings contain built-in locking ears that make any fitting into a Twist-Lok™ cleanout. Twist the cleanout clockwise to slide its hooks over the fitting's ears. Removal later is possible when you need access. The cleanout also fits all standard plastic DWV hubs without the need for cleanout adapters. Since these have no retainer pins, it is held in place by two sheet metal screws, which cut their own threads. For added pressure resistance or protection against casual tampering, the screws also may be used with Genova hubs.

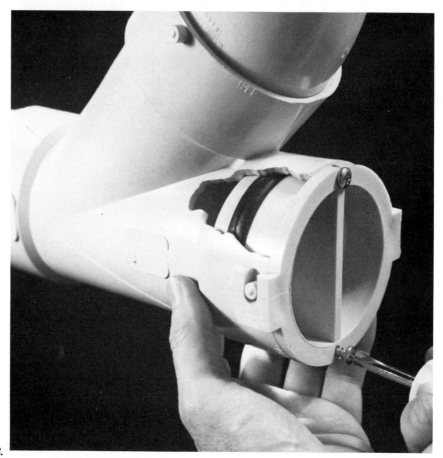

3.

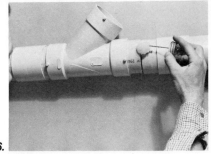

6.

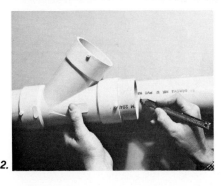

7.

1.

2.

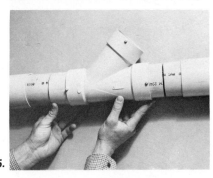

3.

4.

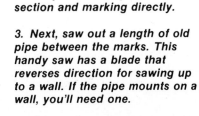

5.

5. Position the new fitting ready for coupling onto the old pipe. Pipe stubs on both ends of the wye are for solvent welding to the slip couplings at either end.

6. Dope the pipe ends all around with as heavy a coating of solvent as you can get. You won't be able to put any solvent inside the slip couplings. Newspapers will catch any runoff.

7. Without delay, slide the slip coupling into place half way astride the joint, giving it a slight twist as you do. Hold the fitting in proper alignment for ten seconds.

1. Two types of Genova DWV couplings: Standard fitting (left) has a shoulder inside to center it on the joint. Without shoulder, slip coupling (right) slides all the way onto a pipe.

2. To join a new DWV run into an existing one, or to make repairs, first mark the portion of the old pipe to be cut out. This is best done by assembling the new section and marking directly.

3. Next, saw out a length of old pipe between the marks. This handy saw has a blade that reverses direction for sawing up to a wall. If the pipe mounts on a wall, you'll need one.

4. Slide a slip coupling onto both ends of the cut pipe, leaving 1½" of the pipe ends exposed for doping. In a pinch, regular couplings could be used by filing away the inside shoulders.

How to Use a Genova Bath Pak

If you're installing a three piece DWV system for a bathroom, you can avoid ordering the fittings separately by getting a Genova Bath Pak. Available in both Schedule 30 In-Wall and Schedule 40, the Bath Pak comes complete with fittings, solvent cement, under-floor tub/shower trap, roof flashing and easy-to-follow instructions. It's furnished in two types for either slab or wood framing installation.

The Bath Pak features Genova's own special waste and vent fitting that can be used with a right-hand or left-hand inlet, or both. Also featured is the Genova Pop-Top™ closet flange.

A sewer adapter connects the new system to 4-inch sewer pipe of clay, cast iron, pitch-fiber, plastic or vinyl.

For many bathroom installations all you need besides a Bath Pak is the pipe. How much of that you'll use depends on how long your pipe runs are. In many cases, 14 feet of 1½-inch and 20 feet of 3-inch pipe will do the job.

See the full list of Bath Pak parts. You may also use it as a checklist for ordering the separate parts of a bathroom installation.

The Bath Pak design assumes that wet-vented waste runs will connect directly to the stack or the special waste and vent fitting as shown in the drawing. If reventing is required, you'll need fittings besides those provided.

A Bath Pak is intended for a single bathroom installation. For two bathrooms either get two Bath Paks (and put away the extra flashing and sewer adapter) or order the parts separately for the second bath.

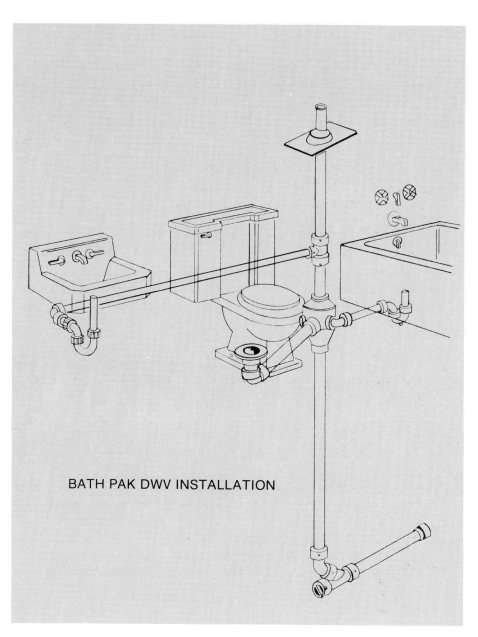

BATH PAK DWV INSTALLATION

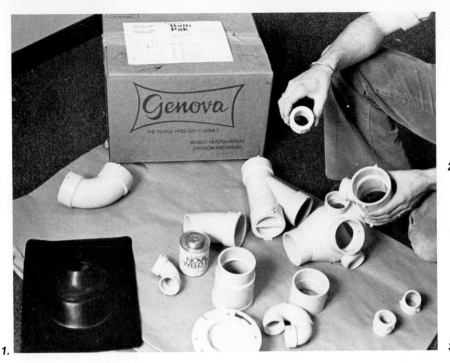

1.

2.

3.

Bath Pak Contents

Qty.	In-Wall Pt. No. 69605	Sch. 40 Pt. No. 79605	Size and Description
1	60130	70130	3″ Coupling
1	70715	70715	1½″ 90° Vent Elbow
1	62830	72830	3″ 90° Sanitary Elbow
1	61030	71030	3″ Wye
1	61131	71131	3″ x 3″ x 1½″ Reducing Sanitary Tee
1	61543*	71543*	4″ Sewer x 3″ IPS Sewer Pipe Adpt. Coupling
1	61873	71873	3″ Twist-Lok™ Cleanout Plug
1	72311	72311	1½″ x 1¼″ Fitting Trap Adapter (Male)
1	72315	72315	1½″ x 1½″ Fitting Trap Adapter (Male)
1	72715	72715	1½″ 45° Street Elbow
1	62730	72730	3″ 45° Street Elbow
1	65134	75134	4″ x 3″ Pop-Top™ Closet Flange
1	67730	77330	3″ x 1½″ Special Waste & Vent Fitting Cap and Bottom
1	78415	78415	1½″ P-Trap w/Cleanout
1	14915	14915	Pint Novaweld P™
1	14563	14563	3″ Snap-Fit™ Roof Flashing

* 61543 & 71543 Coupling Adapts to 4″ Clay, Cast Iron, Fiber and Vinyl Drain Pipe.

1. With a Bath Pak, you get everything you need in one box except the pipe. Spread out on the floor of the bathroom, the parts almost lead you through the easy installation. Directions are included.

2. The first step in installing a Bath Pak kit is planning where the parts will go. A hole has been drilled from the bathroom wall to crawlspace. Special waste and vent fitting is tested for fit.

3. Bath Pak can be prefabricated on the floor, then installed. It's best to dry-fit the parts and test them in place before solvent welding. Once welded, you can't take a joint apart.

Hooking Up Fixtures the Genova Way

Fixture connections in a house plumbed with a Genova drain-waste-vent system of polyvinyl chloride and CPVC or PB water supply system are easy and conventional. Genova materials may be used right up to the fixture drain or faucet. Hook up the drains first, the water supplies last. Here's how:

Toilet waste. Finish out a toilet's waste run at the floor using a toilet flange as described in another chapter. Best of these is the Genova Pop-Top™ closet flange. It comes in several different forms to fit the other parts of a Schedule 30 or 40 DWV system and goes with either wood or concrete floors. The toilet flange should center 12 inches out from the finished bathroom wall (unless you're using an odd-ball toilet with other than the standard 12-inch rough-in).

Place a special toilet hold-down bolt (standard hardware item) in each of the serrated slots of the toilet flange so that a line drawn through the bolts would be parallel to the wall behind the toilet. The flange's slots grab the bolts and hold them upright. Nuts and washers should be removed.

Now, unpack the toilet bowl and rest it upside down on a newspaper cushion. You should have the finished floor material installed and the bathroom wall finished. Place a ring of plumber's putty (another hardware item) around the bowl's outlet horn to seal it to the toilet flange. Be generous; excess putty will squeeze out.

More convenient to use than plumber's putty is a wax toilet gasket made especially for sealing toilet waste connections.

Get the kind without a plastic flange. Place the flat side of the gasket against the toilet bowl.

Finally, lay a slim ring of plumber's putty all around the base of the bowl where it will contact the floor. This seals the floor-bowl joint. Push the ring into firm contact so it won't fall off when you invert the bowl.

Now's the time to pop the top of the Genova toilet flange, if the Pop-Top™ flange was used. Remove the flashing disc and discard it.

Now, invert the toilet bowl, holding it right side up above the flange. Lower it gently onto the flange while watching to see that the two bolts enter their holes in the bowl base. Square up the bowl with the wall as it contacts the floor. Press down, wiggling slightly from side to side and front to back. This squeezes the excess wax and putty out and seats the bowl firmly on the flange and the floor.

Install both hold-down washers and nuts on their bolts. Snug

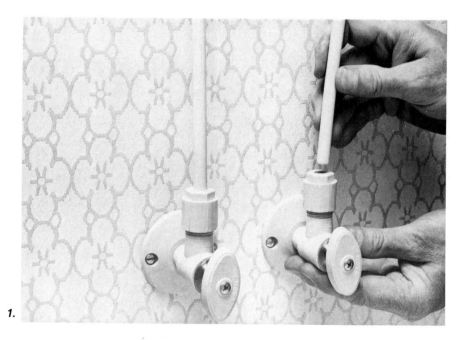

1.

2.

3.

them down with a wrench, being careful not to overtighten (too tight risks cracking the bowl). You don't want them loose, you don't want them tight; you just want them snug.

If the bowl has front mounting holes, install hold-down screws in them. Cover all mounting screws with caps colored to match your toilet. Some caps snap into place while others are set with plumber's putty. Before you finish, clean up any plumber's putty from around the caps and toilet bowl.

Toilet water supply. With the toilet bowl mounted, install the toilet tank on it. An instruction sheet with the toilet usually tells how. (Some toilet bowls have integral tanks and no installation is needed.) Now you're ready to connect the toilet's water supply to its inlet valve.

The water supplies for a toilet and other fixtures should stub out from the wall or floor, preferably with stop valves for emergency shutoff. At the wall use a Genova, Part No. 530651, angle stop. From the floor use a Part No. 530301, straight stop. Both of these handy valves incorporate Genogrip™ adapters, which accept ⅜-inch Genova Poly Risers™. A Poly Riser™ quickly connects the toilet tank with its water supply. A Part No. 530801, 12-inch-long Poly Riser™ will reach in most cases. If not, you can use a 20-inch Part No. 530821, Poly Riser™. It's a stab-in-and-hand-tighten connection at the valve. A toilet's Poly Riser™ is flat-ended to fit the toilet tank inlet. Couple it with a ⅜-inch fixture flange nut. One is often furnished with the toilet. If not, no problem--it's a standard

hardware item. Nothing else is needed. The Poly Riser™ can be cut to length with a knife and is virtually impossible to kink. It will work with a standard ⅜-inch compression or flare fitting, too, as a direct replacement for a flexible copper riser when replacing a fixture in an existing bathroom.

Poly Riser™ installation is the same whether it's being used for a toilet, lavatory or a sink. Measure carefully and cut to length with a knife. Allow for a 1½-inch penetration into the Genogrip™ adapter. Cut clean and square (bevel end slightly). Slide the fixture flange nut up to the molded nosepiece. Draw the nut snug, but not

1. *Patented Poly Risers™, polybutylene tubes with preformed ends, supply lavatories, sinks and toilets.*

2. *Genova Pop-Top™ closet flange screws to the floor. The toilet later will bolt to it for a secure mounting. The flashed-over drain opening seals the DWV system, keeping debris out during construction.*

3. *A few light taps with a hammer will knock out the Pop-Top™ flashing. Do it just before installing the toilet bowl. Discard the disc. The Pop-Top™ also helps in pressure testing the system for water leaks.*

4. *Serrated slots designed into the Genova closet flange grip the toilet hold-down bolts and keep them upright. To engage them, slide the bolts into their slots until both are equidistant from the wall behind the toilet.*

5. *A wax toilet gasket installed around the outlet horn of the toilet bowl seals the connection between toilet bowl and DWV system. The wax gasket, available almost everywhere, is easiest to use for this.*

6. *Lower the prepared bowl squarely onto the toilet flange so that the mounting bolts enter their holes in the bowl's base. The bowl should contact the floor square with the wall and centered on the flange.*

4.

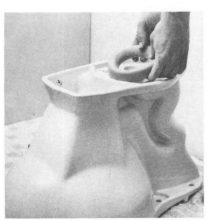

5.

6.

1.

2.

3.

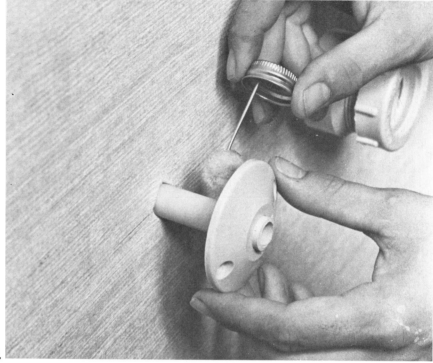

4.

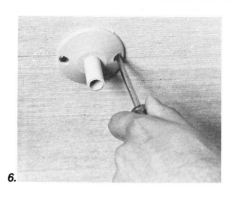

6.

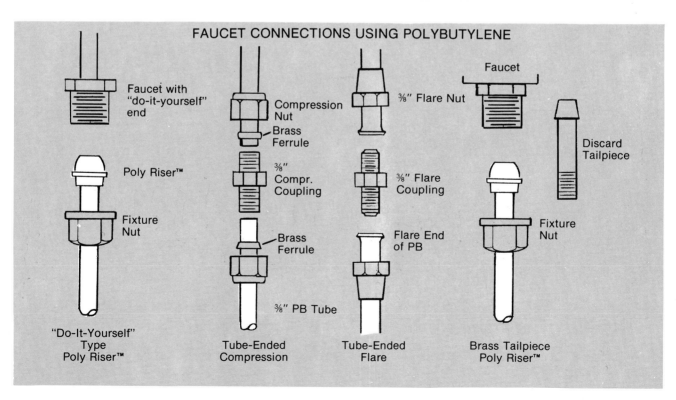

5.

FAUCET CONNECTIONS USING POLYBUTYLENE

Faucet with "do-it-yourself" end

Poly Riser™

Fixture Nut

"Do-It-Yourself" Type Poly Riser™

Compression Nut

Brass Ferrule

⅜" Compr. Coupling

Brass Ferrule

⅜" PB Tube

Tube-Ended Compression

⅜" Flare Nut

⅜" Flare Coupling

Flare End of PB

Tube-Ended Flare

Faucet

Discard Tailpiece

Fixture Nut

Brass Tailpiece Poly Riser™

overly tight. Bend the riser in a smooth curve and slide it into the Genogrip™ fitting. Finally, tighten the handnut. Turn on the stop valve to check for leaks.

Lavatory waste. All lavatory and sink bowls, drains, pop-up drains and faucets should be installed following the instructions that come with them. Use plumber's putty under both sides of bowl flanges, around drains and beneath faucets not having base gaskets. This gets you ready for drain connection.

Waste stub-outs to lavatories and sinks may begin inside the finished wall with 1½-inch trap adapters, also called Marvel couplings. It may be a Genova Part No. 72315, which solvent welds into a 1½-inch PVC waste fitting socket. Or, it may be a Part No. 72215, which joins onto a 1½-inch PVC waste pipe. It may also be in the form of a Part No. 73217, 1½-inch, or a No. 73218, 1½" x 1¼" Marvel Elbow. (See the chapter on DWV plumbing for examples on how fixture waste stub-outs may be handled.)

Stub-outs for fixtures also may begin with a plain 1½-inch pipe end to which a Genova, Part No. 176151, P-Trap is solvent welded.

All trap adapters will accept both metal and plastic traps. We recommend the use of Genova

100 Series 1½-inch poly-propylene P-traps (or S-traps if the trap must run to the floor instead of the wall). Each Genova trap adapter comes with a heavy-duty slip jam nut and a thermoplastic jam nut washer.

If you already have a smaller 1¼-inch lavatory trap and wish to use it, you may. Simply get a Part No. 148111, 1½" x 1¼" reducing jam nut washer and mount your trap to the 1½-inch trap adapter using it and the regular slip jam nut.

Another Genova fitting, the Part No. 73218, Marvel elbow, comes ready to accept a 1¼-inch lavatory trap. Nothing else is needed. It will not fit a 1½-inch trap, however, so don't use it for plumbing a kitchen sink.

Genova 1½-inch traps are furnished with extra 1½ x 1¼-inch reducing washers for use with lavatories. The washer adapts the 1¼-inch lavatory tailpiece to the 1½-inch trap inlet. The tailpiece is threaded finely at one end. Put some plumber's putty on the threads and screw it into the threaded lavatory drain. Hand-tighten. Install the trap's slip jam nut over the tailpiece then slide the reducing washer on the end of the tailpiece. Now the trap inlet and tailpieces will join perfectly, even though they're different sizes.

1. Connect the toilet tank with a Poly Riser™ and tank nut, usually furnished with the toilet. Light wrench-tightening should make it leak-free. A plumbing manifold supplies this installation from the toilet's wall.

2. Two types of Poly Risers™ simplify the hookup of fixtures to their water supply. The bullet-nosed one (left) is for lavatories, sinks. The flat ended one is for toilets. A fixture flange nut does the coupling.

3. Water supply stub-outs behind fixtures should end in stop valves having Genogrip™ fittings. One end of these solvent welds to the ½" CPVC stub-out. Align Genogrip™ fittings facing upward aimed toward the fixture.

4. If stop valves must be located in the floor beneath a fixture, install a straight stop having a Genogrip™ adapter. These and Poly Risers™ make the greatest combination yet for fixture water supply hookup.

5. To relieve the twisting force exerted on CPVC pipes stubbed through finished walls, use Genova's specially constructed wall escutcheon, Torque Flange™.

6. Solvent weld it to the thru-the-wall pipe stub and then anchor to the dry wall with screws.

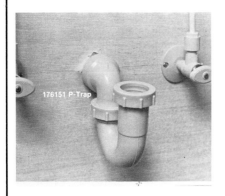

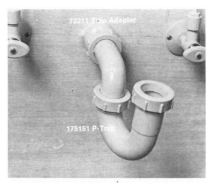

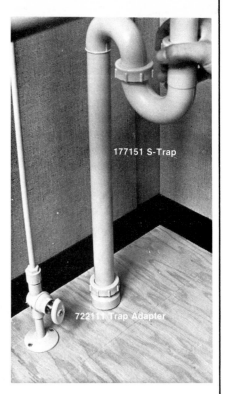

TRAPS AND TRAP ADAPTERS

Assemble the two trap parts angled or straight as needed to allow the long trap arm to enter the waste pipe and trap adapter straight on. With all parts aligned, tighten the slip jam nuts at both ends and in the center of the trap.

Genova recommends the use of plumber's putty inside all slip nut connections to keep them leak-free. The plastic parts of Genova traps are unaffected by the mineral oils in putty. On the other hand, ordinary ABS plastic traps and slip jam nuts suffer stress cracking, an inter-granular structural failure that is accelerated by organic compounds. For this reason, plumber's putty should not be used on this material. The trick works only on Genova and metal traps.

Another good trap joint sealer is silicone rubber sealant, the type used for house caulking, bathtubs and aquariums. It's for metal and Genova traps only though. The silicone attacks ABS plastic traps.

Genova *100 Series* poly-propylene traps resist all house-hold chemicals and solvents. They outperform metal traps, though they install in the same manner, and they cost less. Tailpieces (1½-inch) as well as extension tailpieces are available. All work together.

Sink waste. A kitchen sink's waste connection installs the same as a lavatory waste connection except that tailpiece size is 1½ inches. Traps used with a sink should also be 1½-inch.

For hooking up double com-partment kitchen sinks and feeding their wastes into a single trap, Genova markets the Part No. 186001, end opening continuous waste. Using it, the trap is located on one side. If the trap is to be centered under a double sink, use the Part No. 186101, center opening waste.

For connecting a waste disposal unit or other drain to a double compartment sink, add the Part No. 186301, disposal baffle tee. For connecting a dishwasher drain under the kitchen sink, use the Part No. 138401, dishwasher tailpiece. Genova builds lots of parts to help you plumb.

1.

2.

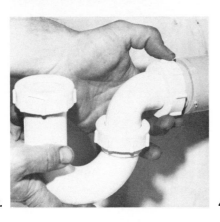

3.

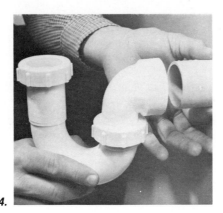

4.

1. Shower drains, being two inches, do not connect with slip jam nuts. They require caulking. Rope oakum is packed in tightly, leaving one inch of pipe exposed above it. Space is then filled with Genova Plastic Lead Seal.

2. A neat way to make sure that trap assemblies stay leak-free is to run silicone sealant around the joints before you put them together. Silicone will not harm Genova polypropylene or metal fixture traps.

3. & 4. Two types of Genova polypropylene traps are made to suit the type of installation you are making. Most useful is the regular version (3.), which connects to a trap adapter at the waste pipe with a slip jam nut. The Genova P-trap solvent welds directly to the 1½" waste pipe without a trap adapter or nut (4.). Since its reach is not adjustable, the waste pipe must be installed to the correct length.

Lavatory/sink supply. The hot and cold water supplies to sinks and lavatories start with an angle stop at the wall or a straight stop at the floor. Genova water supply stop valves with Genogrip™ adapters are designed for direct solvent welded connection to a CPVC water supply system. (See toilet water supply on page 49.) They mate with Genova Poly Risers™ for easy sink and lavatory hookup. Get the length you need. The Part No. 530841, Poly Riser™ comes with two 12-inch-long risers to a package. Part No. 530861 comprises a pair of risers 20 inches long and Part No. 530881 is a pair 36 inches long. All have bullet-nosed ends spin welded on for direct connection to most lavatory and sink faucets.

To use Poly Risers™ with faucets having plain ended, copper tubes, cut off the shaped ends and flare the risers. Also, flare the end of the faucet tube (flare nut installed first) and join the riser and the faucet tube with a ⅜-inch flare coupling. If the faucet supplies are ¼-inch, as many lavatory faucets are, use a ¼ x ⅜-inch flare adapter coupling to make the connection.

Compression couplings, rather than flare, may be used if you prefer. With them no flaring is required. You can use regular brass ferrules.

On sink faucets having short threaded tailpieces coupled with fixture nuts, discard the tailpieces and connect the bullet-nosed Poly Risers™ directly to the faucet using the same nuts.

Tub/shower connections. Bathtubs and showers are fixtures, too, but they connect slightly differently from lavs, sinks and toilets. For a tub's trap use a Genova *700 Series* 1½-inch P-trap. The two parts solvent weld together at the angle that best suits installation. A metal tub-drain tailpiece (comes with the tub-drain hardware) enters a Part No. 72315, trap adapter installed in the trap's inlet end

by solvent welding. Or, an even simpler method is to use Genova's Part No. 176151, polypropylene trap. It has a special elbow which welds right onto the 1½-inch PVC drain pipe.

For a shower, install a 2-inch PVC pipe solvent welded into the *700 Series* trap inlet and reaching up to the shower drain fitting and into it. There it either solvent welds to a Part No. 71470 shower drain (for ceramic built-in shower applications) or it is oakum-caulked and plastic-lead-sealed into a conventional metal shower floor drain fitting.

Where the bottom of the P-traps are accessible from below, it's best to use the kind with cleanouts. Otherwise that feature is not usable.

Tub/shower water supplies are adapted to a ½-inch CPVC system using transition adapters. Pipe the shower head from the shower valve as shown on page 32. Because the spout is subject to some hard knocks, I recommend hooking it up to the faucet manifold with metal nipples. Galvanized will do, but brass eliminates any possibility of rusty water. Don't forget to build air chambers for the hot and cold water supplies to prevent overpressures when the tub/shower valve is turned off quickly.

Other fixtures such as dishwashers, drinking fountains and water coolers may be connected using Genogrip™ angle stops, PB flexible supply tubes (or Poly Risers™) and adapters at the fixture of appliance.

For automatic washer hookup, see pages 70-71.

2.

3.

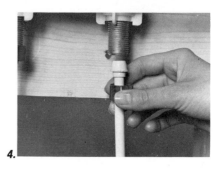

4.

1. To connect a fixture's water supply with Genova Poly Risers™, each riser is cut to length with a knife. Make the cut square and remove any burrs. Be sure to allow enough riser length for smooth bends.

2. Stab the cut end of the Poly Riser™ into the loosened Genogrip™ adapter. It should enter all the way, bottoming out on the shoulder inside the adapter. The shoulder is there to prevent overinsertion of the riser.

3. Hand-tighten the nut on the adapter, bringing its patented grip-ring tight around the PB tube. A ridge inside the ring indents the tube wall, preventing pull-out or blow-out of the PB riser from its connection.

4. The last step is to connect the Poly Riser™ to the fixture. The bullet-shaped end of the lavatory/sink Poly Riser™ makes a watertight seal with most faucet tailpieces using a fixture flange nut to couple them.

1.

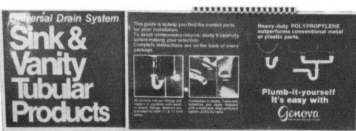

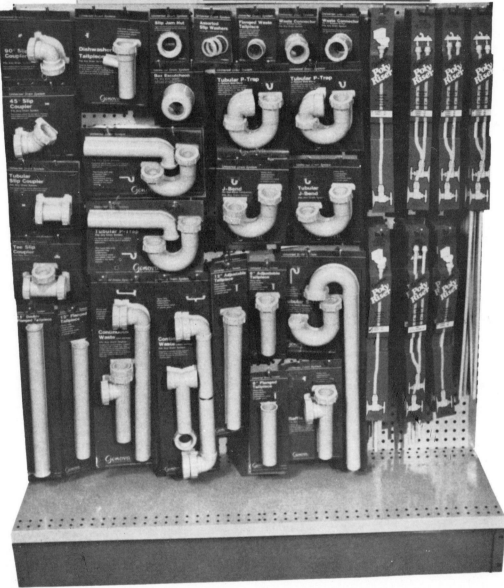

Building a PVC Sewer-Septic System

If you live outside a city, you'll probably have need for a private sewage disposal facility called a septic system. Done the easy Genova way, a septic system comprises a sewer line leading from the house, a septic tank and a seepage field. The septic tank is where solid and liquid household wastes decompose by bacterial action. Solids settle out or float while the resultant liquid, called effluent, flows out into the seepage field. There it is absorbed into the ground.

The entire septic system is built below the ground. All piping slopes from the house toward the far end of the seepage field for gravity flow.

Genova makes all the pipes and fittings needed for building a septic system. The septic tank can be put together in the ground or purchased prebuilt and placed in a hole for you by the seller. Genova's *400 Series* sewer pipe and fittings are the ones for building a sewer-septic system. Pipes are four to six inches in diameter and ten feet long. You can use the 4-inch size for a single-family residence.

Use solid-wall pipe for sewers and tight lines between the septic tank and seepage bed; use perforated pipe for seepage lines. Fittings for both are the same and they are available in a complete assortment.

1.

Genova markets a beige-colored sewer-septic system pipe of exceptional quality. One end of each pipe is enlarged as a self-coupler. Thus, no couplings are needed for joining one pipe to another. Genova PVC sewer pipes may be coupled by any one of two methods: solvent welding and dry assembling. Dry assembling without solvent welding serves seepage lines. Genova PVC sewer pipe comes in both solid-wall and perforated. It works with all Genova *400 Series* fittings.

2.

3.

4.

5.

SEPTIC SYSTEM DESIGN

You stand to save considerable money by building your own septic system. Unless you enjoy digging, though, hire the holes for the septic tank and seepage bed dug by machine. Before you start, check with local public health authorities for advice on meeting their requirements.

Correct sizing for the septic tank is important. No tank should be less than 750 gallons, that for a two-bedroom house. For three bedrooms, make the tank at least 900 gallons. Four bedrooms, 1,000 gallons. Beyond that add 250 gallons of tank capacity for each additional bedroom. These sizes are minimums. They have capacity to handle wastes from a garbage disposal, an automatic washing machine and other common water-using appliances.

We recommend a two compartment septic tank, as shown in the drawing, because it functions more efficiently and needs cleaning less often. If you build the tank yourself, follow the general details for the concrete block tank shown. Size for the required gallonage of your tank. There are some seven and one-half gallons in one cubic foot.

All elements of the septic system must be located to meet minimum distance requirements. The septic tank should be at least five feet from the house, ten feet from any lot line. Other parts of the system should be a minimum of eight feet from the house and ten feet from lot lines. Keep the seepage field at least 100 feet from a well and the rest of the system at least 50 feet away.

Percolation test. Another sizing question concerns the seepage field. Too small, it will overload the soil with effluent and "break out" on the surface. Too large a seepage field, of course, uses up money you'll want for other projects.

A seepage field's size for proper effluent disposal depends both on the amount of water to be disposed of and the ability of the soil to absorb it. Tight clay soils absorb little effluent; loose sandy soils absorb lots. The number of bedrooms a house has is a good guide to the amount of water to be handled, but the best way to find your soil's absorptive ability is to test it yourself. Some health regs call for such a check, called a percolation test, or simply

1. Light, easy-to-handle 10-foot lengths of Genova 400 Series PVC pipe could not be easier to install. For a tight-joint sewer line you may use solvent weld couplings (shown).

2. Genova sewer-septic system pipe (left) is thinner walled than Schedule 40 DWV pipe (right). While it should not be used for indoor DWV purposes, sewer pipe is excellent for underground use.

3. Genova 400 Series pipe comes two ways: perforated for seepage lines (top) and solid walled for sewer and other tight lines. A complete selection of fittings is also available.

4. Solvent welding of pipe joints may be done either in the trench or on top of the ground. Follow the usual procedure. Out-of-trench welds need 12 hours curing before lowering the pipes.

5. With both pipe end and fitting socket coated with Novaweld™ cement, join them with a slight twist and hold 10 seconds. The pipe end is supported off the ground to keep it clean during the process.

perc test. While officials may want the test to be made by a professional, hold out for doing it yourself. The pro charges a lot. Here's how you can make a perc test:

Dig at least six test holes around the area you plan to use for the seepage field. They should be downslope from the house for a good gravity flow from it to the field. Holes may be four to twelve inches in diameter. Dig them the same depth your seepage bed will be, often 36 inches. Space holes uniformly over the whole seepage bed area. Roughen the sides of each hole to help absorb water. Remove loose dirt, adding two inches of sand or gravel to the bottom of each hole.

Now run at least a 12-inch depth of water into every hole. Add more water, as necessary, to keep the water level above the bottom for at least four hours.

Finally, adjust the water level in each hole to six inches above the bottom. Then measure the drop in water level over a 30-minute period. Multiply that by two to get inches of fall per hour. That's your soil's percolation rate. Average the rate for all holes.

If water seeps into the holes as you dig them, the water table is too high for successful septic system operation.

If water will not stay in the holes overnight, count yourself lucky and use this alternate measuring procedure: Add water to a 6-inch depth. Add more water as often as needed to keep it about six inches deep for three and one-half hours. Then measure the drop in level during the next 30 minutes, doubling that to arrive at the per hour perc rate.

In really fast perking, sandy soils, you're really lucky. There you need hold the levels for only 50 minutes at six inches, measuring the level's drop over a period of ten minutes following. Multiply by six to get your perc rate.

Tight soils with a percolation rate of less than an inch per hour are unsuitable for use as a seepage field. Either find a better location or switch your plans to a private sewage treatment plant. (Consult public health officials on that.)

Now an example: If the perc rate measures three inches an hour, you'll find from the accompanying graph that 200 square feet of absorption area is needed for each bedroom. A three-bedroom house would thus need 600 square feet of seepage bed. That's an area 20 by 30 feet.

Instead of a seepage bed, you may install seepage trenches or seepage pits. Trenches work a bit better than a bed because the sides as well as the bottom of the trench absorb effluent. Seepage pits are deep holes in the ground lined on the exterior with porous masonry or concrete. They're used to solve special disposal problems such as reaching down through a bad-acting surface soil to a better-acting subsoil where successful seepage can take place.

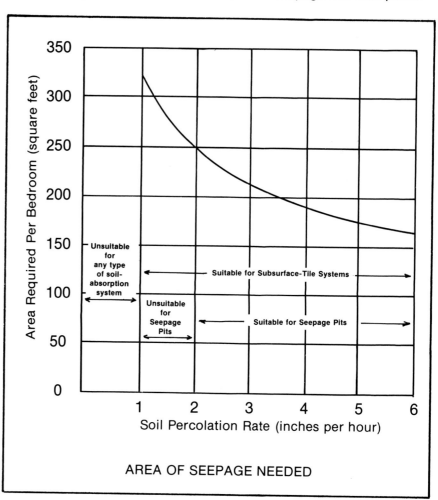

AREA OF SEEPAGE NEEDED

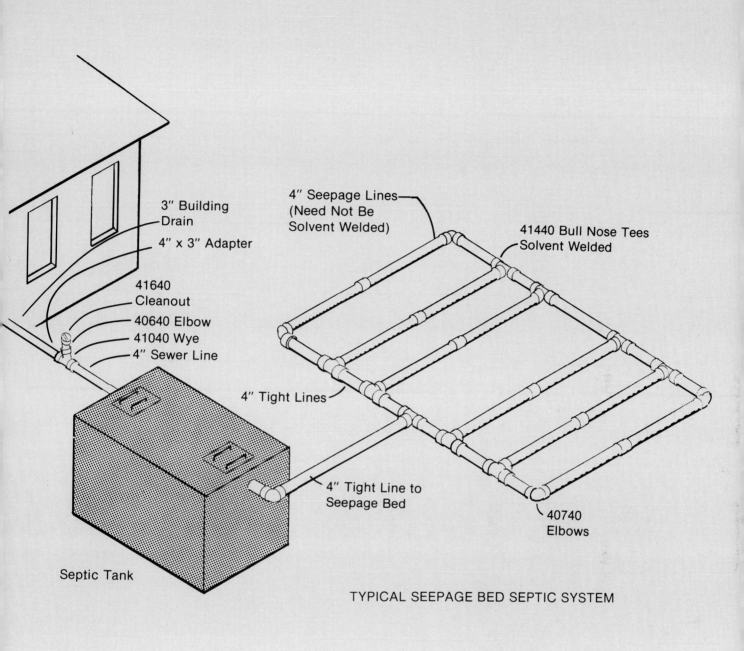

3" Building Drain

4" x 3" Adapter

41640 Cleanout

40640 Elbow

41040 Wye

4" Sewer Line

4" Seepage Lines (Need Not Be Solvent Welded)

41440 Bull Nose Tees Solvent Welded

4" Tight Lines

4" Tight Line to Seepage Bed

40740 Elbows

Septic Tank

TYPICAL SEEPAGE BED SEPTIC SYSTEM

Build the sewer. Once designed and approved, your septic system can get under construction. Start at the house. Code permitting, we recommend that you simply continue the 3- or 4-inch building drain all the way to the septic tank. The most modern codes now okay Genova Schedule 30 In-Wall pipe for this below-ground use. Extension saves adapting to a larger-sized sewer pipe. Be sure the slope is at least ¼-inch per foot to keep a good flow moving through the smaller pipe.

If you increase a 3-inch building drain to 4-inch sewer pipe, do it with a Part No. 71543 adapter for 3-inch Schedule 40 or a Part No. 61543 adapter for Schedule 30. Both adapt to *400 Series* sewer pipe by solvent welding.

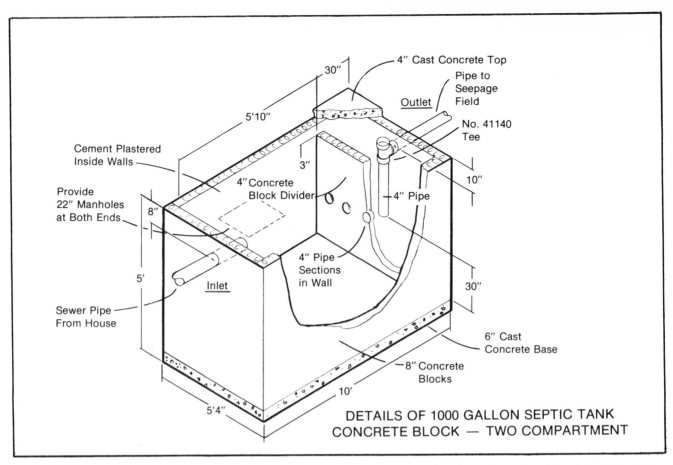

30″
5′10″
4″ Cast Concrete Top
Pipe to Seepage Field
Outlet
No. 41140 Tee
Cement Plastered Inside Walls
4″ Concrete Block Divider
3″
10″
Provide 22″ Manholes at Both Ends
8″
4″ Pipe
4″ Pipe Sections in Wall
5′
30″
Inlet
Sewer Pipe From House
6″ Cast Concrete Base
8″ Concrete Blocks
5′4″
10′

DETAILS OF 1000 GALLON SEPTIC TANK
CONCRETE BLOCK — TWO COMPARTMENT

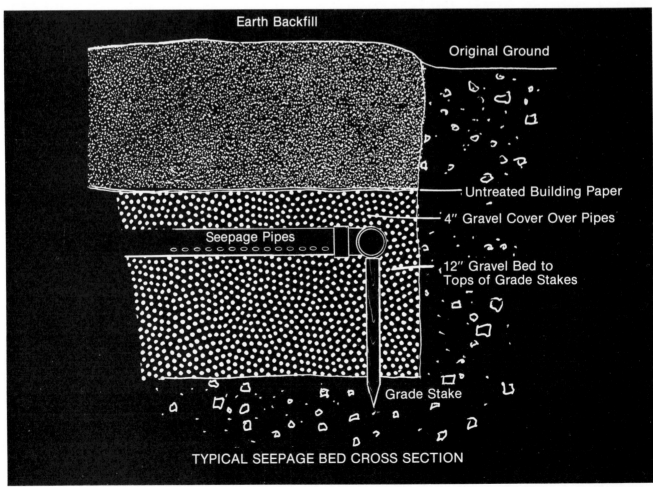

Earth Backfill
Original Ground
Untreated Building Paper
4″ Gravel Cover Over Pipes
Seepage Pipes
12″ Gravel Bed to Tops of Grade Stakes
Grade Stake

TYPICAL SEEPAGE BED CROSS SECTION

1. Purchased precast concrete septic tank is lowered into a predug hole in the ground by the truck that delivered it. Firms selling such tanks can furnish details on the size of hole required.

In the basement, crawlspace or outside the foundation, provide a cleanout for the horizontal house-to-septic tank sewer line. An outside ground-level cleanout works through a wye and Twist-Lok™ cleanout fitting, as shown in the drawing. No cleanout is needed for effluent lines. No vents are needed, either, since house roof venting of the DWV system does that job.

Dig the sewer trench a few inches deeper than required and replace the excess with pea gravel or selected earth. Earth fill should be free from rocks and frozen lumps. Dampen and compact it. Slope all fill uniformly before laying the sewer line on it. Dig out for fittings so that the line rests on the pipes, not just on the fittings. Also see that no pipe must bridge depressions in the trench bottom or cross unexcavated bumps.

The sewer line may be assembled either in the trench or on top of the ground. We recommend doing it on the ground. That's easier. However, then you should wait 12 hours after solvent welding before lowering the assembled line into the trench. The reason for the delay is to allow the joints to gain strength before subjecting them to the powerful leverages encountered in the lowering operation. To bypass the 12-hour wait, solvent weld on the trench bottom. In any case, use Novaclean™ primer followed by Novaweld P™ solvent, keeping dirt out of the joints.

Backfill around the sewer pipe with pea gravel or selected earth backfill. If you use an earth backfill, tamp it lightly around the pipe. See that no rocks come in contact with the pipe. Final backfill merely needs to be free of large rocks and foreign objects.

Tank connections. The top of the septic tank should be at least a foot below ground, two to three feet in heavy-frost climates. Don't get the tank too deep, however, because its access holes must be dug up for inspection and possible cleaning every two years or so. If the septic tank is not equipped with pipe fittings at its inlet end, go right into it with the PVC sewer pipe. Mortar can be used to seal the space between pipe and a concrete or masonry tank. Genova recommends that no elbow or tee be used on the tank inlet. End fittings normally installed there invite plugging, the firm's experts believe.

At the outlet end of a fittingless septic tank, install a Part No. 41140, PVC tee with a drop pipe as shown in the drawing. This should reach at least 18 inches below the liquid level. Genova's experts say that it can extend to within a foot of the tank bottom. The top of the tee is left open for venting of the seepage field.

If your septic tank comes with inlet and outlet fittings already installed, you can adapt to them. Most often clay pipe fittings are used, in which case you connect with a Part No. 41540, clay-to-vinyl adapter. To adapt to cast iron fittings, use a Part No. 41740 vinyl-to-cast-iron-spigot adapter. Adapters are caulked to their fittings.

Seepage field. Join the outlet tee through the wall of the septic tank with a 6-foot length of PVC solid-wall sewer pipe and then install a Part No. 41440, bull-nose tee level to start a grid seepage bed system. Use solid wall pipe, perforated pipe, elbows and bull nose tees to build a grid system similar to the one shown in the drawing. It should be large enough to cover your seepage bed.

Seepage pipe perforations should be placed on the bottom. Using Genova pipe, when you can see the printing topside, you know that the perforations are down. It's another helpful Genova feature.

Seepage pipe and fittings need not be solvent welded, though they may be if you wish. A push-on fit is okay.

To prevent effluent back-up in seepage lines, they need to be sloped from two to four inches per 100 feet. That isn't much, some codes require that seepage lines be level.

On sloping land seepage trenches should follow contour lines of the ground.

When the area for the seepage bed has been excavated, put in about 12 inches of gravel and grade it out evenly. Smallest size stones should be ½ inch, the largest 2½ inches. Build the seepage grid on the gravel. Backfill around the grid with more gravel to at least four inches above the pipes. Then spread a covering of untreated building paper or straw to prevent soil infiltration into the gravel layers. Finally, backfill with earth.

Of course, you may need to have the system inspected before backfill. Also, a final inspection of the whole system may be required.

Seepage trenches, if you use them, should be from 12 to 36 inches wide and spaced at least six feet apart, better ten feet.

1.

2.

3.

They're normally three feet deep. Generally, no trench should be longer than 100 feet. Use several of them instead. The seepage area of a trench is calculated as width of trench times length in feet. Pipe-laying and backfill are the same as for a seepage bed.

If properly designed, built and maintained, your septic system should be effective for many years.

4.

5.

6.

7.

8.

9.

1. Seepage line construction starts with the hardest part-- digging. Seepage trenches require far less excavation than a seepage bed shown in the drawings. Working by hand, you'll want a trenched system.

2. Install grade stakes in the bottom of the 3-foot deep trench. For good flow these should slope slightly away from the septic tank. Same with the trench bottom. Stakes stick up about a foot.

3. A carpenter's level taped to a length of straight 2″ x 4″, long enough to span between grade stakes, helps establish their slope. A 1/16″ shim under one end of a 2′ level will give about a 3″ per 100′ slope.

4. Fill the trench bottom with stones to the tops of the grade stakes. The stakes are used to help get a uniform slope to the gravel. Stones should be ½″ to 2½″ in diameter.

5. A trenched seepage field needs a distribution box to divide effluent equally among two or more tile lines. Precast con- crete unit is leveled in the ground. Highest hole is the inlet, lower ones are outlets.

6. Perforated seepage lines begin 5′ from the distribution box. Lay them on the gravel touching grade stakes. Pipe perforations should be down, printing topside. Dry coupling is permissible.

7. Backfill over the seepage pipe with another layer of stones. Build this up at least 4″ above the pipe. Construction of a seepage bed is similar, except it uses a large hole with a gridwork of pipes.

8. A large rock placed blocking the end of a seepage pipe completes a run. The rock keeps stone backfill from entering the pipe. Such a closure is not necessary in a seepage-bed gridwork.

9. Roll out a layer of building paper on top of the stone fill to keep subsequent soil backfill from infiltrating. Soil may be mounded so that later settlement brings it flush with the ground.

Installing Genova Sump Pumps

Credit Genova with the most innovative sump pump on the market today. Made of noncorroding vinyl, the Genova Sump Witch™ solves the number one problem of all sump pumps-- switch failure. Internal electrical circuitry is protected against corrosion. The Sump Witch™ utilizes a new hermetically sealed floating ball and raceway switch, which will last for more than a million cycles. That's a hundred years of average use in a rainy climate . . . and then some. So good is the Sump Witch™ that the firm has phased out its other sump pumps.

The Sump Witch™ comes in two models: upright and submersible. The upright model is comprised of four modules-- base, bearing-drive shaft assembly, power head, and switch. The more compact submersible model is made up of only three modules--base, power head, and switch. Both Sump Witch™ models make enlightened use of vinyl, so much that Genova dares to compare the Sump Witch™ to long-life, and much more expensive, brass sump pumps. "A Cadillac at a Chevrolet price," the advertising reads.

Because of the modular design of Sump Witch™ sump pumps, it is not necessary to replace an entire pump in the event of problems, only the defective module. Replacement modules are available through Genova's large network of authorized Sump Witch™ dealers. The Sump Witch™ has been designed for reliability, with ease and simplicity of rarely needed maintenance in mind.

Modular design. Both pumps' power head module contain all 1.

the moving parts. The upright pump's power head contains the unique bearing-drive shaft assembly module, easily removed in the event of service or replacement. With the more compact submersible power head, the motor shaft is directly connected to the all vinyl pump impeller. Both module power heads fasten into an identical base module with simple bayonet lugs and a Twist-Lok™ action.

To remove the power module for flushing out debris from the base and pump housing, you just grasp the motor and twist clockwise one-quarter turn. It lifts out. The vinyl mating surfaces can never corrode. The procedure is reversed to replace the power module back in the base module. Motor rotation acts in the "lock" direction. Genova labels this its "twist-apart" feature.

The power module's inlet boasts top intake design. With this, water must flow up over the base to reach the intake strainer, minimizing the clogging effect of debris inside the sump. Debris tends to settle on the bottom of the sump rather than be drawn up and into the impeller.

Since the upright model uses a specially designed vinyl-plastic drive shaft and rigid vinyl support column, motor and water are electrically isolated. In the submersible model the motor is sealed and insulated by a reservoir of oil, thus eliminating ordinary shock hazard.

Power module removal requires no tools and no removal of the discharge piping--a great time-saver in pump maintenance.

The pump's base module is designed to be easy to flush out. Extra large, it gives the pump a good footing, yet will fit into most sumps now in use.

The switch module is the "brain" of the pump. The patented Some Switch™ mounts on the column of the upright and on the motor housing of the submersible. It contains a snap-action switch inside the seated vinyl float chamber. As the switch chamber swings up and down with sump water level, a polished steel ball running on a raceway inside rolls into and out of contact with the snap-action switch arm. "Hunting," switching on and off under turbulent water conditions, is avoided.

Like the others, the switch module can be attached or removed without tools. Rather than connecting directly to the sump pump motor, the switch contains a piggyback plug/receptacle. The motor's lead, in turn, plugs into the piggyback. This permits plugging of the motor lead directly into the electrical outlet to test motor operation. It also permits manual control of the pump, if desired.

The Some Switch™ also is sold as a replacement for a failed switch on any sump pump or a fluid level control in a variety of applications. Ask for Part No. 95010.

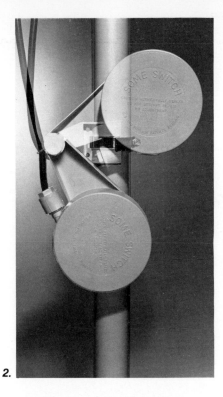

2.

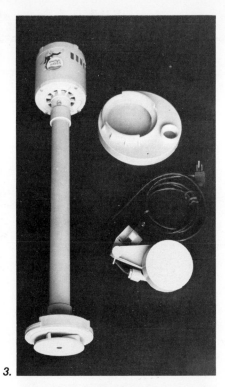

3.

1. Take your choice of Genova Sump Witch™ sump pumps-- upright (left) or submersible (right). Both feature modular, noncorroding vinyl construction and come with the sealed, trouble-free Some Switch™.

2. Some Switch™ has a unique patented design which incorporates a highly reliable snap-action switch of the type used in aerospace applications. The rise of liquid level causes the float arm to rise to its highest point and close the switch circuit. It is hermetically sealed to eliminate electrical shock and arcing hazards and to insulate it from outside contamination.

3. & 4. The motor, switch and base modules on the upright (3.) and the submersible (4.) fit together without tools for easy installation or removal.

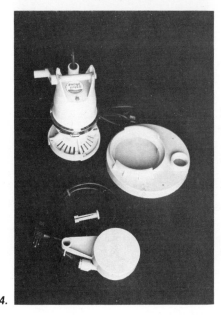

4.

PUMP INSTALLATION

Sump pumps operate in such a corrosive atmosphere that most do not last very long. The Genova Sump Witch™ has been built to avoid that drawback.

Be sure that the pump rests level in the sump. Clean out large stones and other debris. Position and secure the pump so that the discharge pipe and switch are farthest from the sump wall to ensure that switch action will not be hampered by contact with the sump.

The Genova Universal Check Valve. Every sump pump installation should have a check valve to prevent wasteful backflow of water inside the discharge pipe. The Genova Part No. 96630, Universal Check Valve is made to adapt directly to 1¼-inch polyethylene pipe, which is often used for sump pump discharge connections, or it will solvent weld to a 1½-inch PVC discharge pipe. An 1½-inch PVC coupling does the trick. You can go from there with 1½-inch PVC. The Universal Check Valve also fits a 1¼-inch corrugated sump pump discharge kit, which is widely available. Should you use a corrugated hose discharge kit, be sure that the pump is secured so that it does "walk" as it cycles. Motor starting torque will sometimes cause the pump to change its position in the sump if it is not secured. This can result in the switch operation being impaired, so watch out. The valve comes furnished with two flexible couplers and the necessary clamps for flexible hookups too!

1. Universal Check Valve

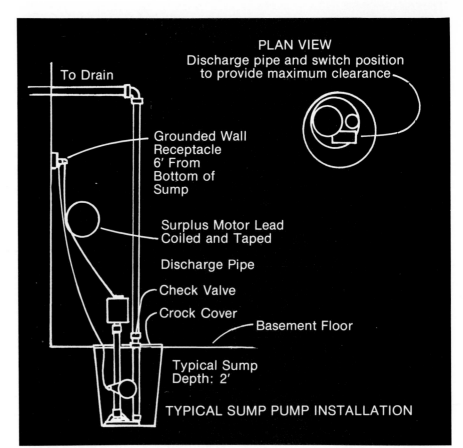

PLAN VIEW
Discharge pipe and switch position to provide maximum clearance

To Drain

Grounded Wall Receptacle 6' From Bottom of Sump

Surplus Motor Lead Coiled and Taped

Discharge Pipe

Check Valve

Crock Cover

Basement Floor

Typical Sump Depth: 2'

TYPICAL SUMP PUMP INSTALLATION

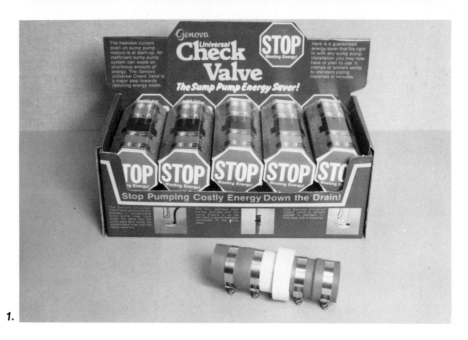

1.

The drawings show four ways of sump discharge hookup. Genova recommends screwing the Universal Check Valve directly into the threaded pump discharge outlet then coming out of the sump pit with 1½-inch PVC solvent welded discharge piping. The flexible reinforced plastic driveshaft makes the Sump Witch™ self-silencing. Also, the twist-out feature lets the pump be removed from the sump without affecting the base module. Both features combine to negate the advantage of a flexible discharge hookup, although one may still be used, if desired. The rigid discharge installation is superior because it doesn't have flexible piping to interfere with switch operation.

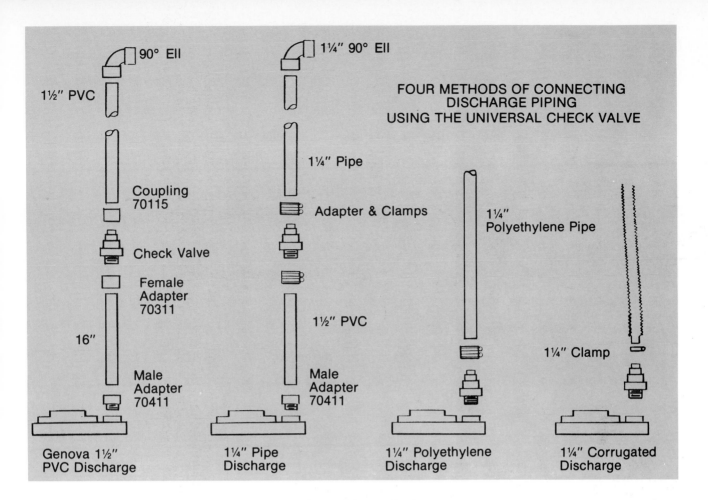

90° Ell

1½" PVC

1¼" 90° Ell

FOUR METHODS OF CONNECTING DISCHARGE PIPING USING THE UNIVERSAL CHECK VALVE

Coupling 70115

1¼" Pipe

Check Valve

Adapter & Clamps

1¼" Polyethylene Pipe

Female Adapter 70311

16"

1½" PVC

Male Adapter 70411

Male Adapter 70411

1¼" Clamp

Genova 1½" PVC Discharge

1¼" Pipe Discharge

1¼" Polyethylene Discharge

1¼" Corrugated Discharge

Sump crock. If you're installing a new sump pump from scratch, you'll need a crock or lined pit for it in the basement floor. (Sometimes, when only a basement laundry is to be drained, the sump crock is set on top of the floor.) Ideal for an in- or on-floor installation is the Genova Polycrock. It's made of unbreakable heavy gauge polyethylene. The 18-gallon crock comes with a safety lid. Holes are blind-formed in the lid for both discharge pipe and upright column. Side cutouts, anywhere you care to make them, accept drain pipes entering the crock. Later, pouring of concrete around on in-floor crock seals the openings between pipes and crock.

The sump pump's electrical connection needs a 15-ampere grounding-type receptacle. Never cut off the pump's grounding pin to allow it to be used in an old-style nongrounding outlet. That can be dangerous.

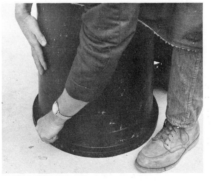

1.

2.

1. Best basement sump pump installation is in the floor. Mark around the sump crock for the opening.

2. Chip out the floor opening to the size marked. Use a cold chisel and hammer, wearing goggles. Also, dig out below the floor for the crock.

1.

2.

3.

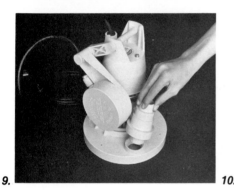

5.

6.

7.

9.

10.

11.

Maintenance. Sump pump maintenance should be done during the dry season before the pump is needed. Maintenance consists of a check of motor operation by pulling the motor plug from the piggyback plug receptacle and inserting it directly into the house receptacle for manual operation. Don't run the pump for more than a few seconds, as it may be dry and the lower bearing is designed for water lubrication.

Unplug the pump and switch entirely and remove any large debris that may have gotten into the sump.

Finally, plug the pump in again and flush out the sump with a hose, letting the pump run to evacuate flush water.

NEVER reach into the sump or handle the sump pump while it is plugged in. That's exposing yourself needlessly to shock hazard, which can kill.

The submersible pump costs about 25 percent more than the upright Sump Witch™, but it has the ability to run under water. In the unlikely event of being inundated with more water than can be pumped or starting up after a power failure, a submersible would still be on the job. An upright sump will probably fail if the water level reaches its motor. It could even constitute an electrical hazard in that case.

For these reasons, I recommend spending the extra money and getting a submersible Sump Witch™. It offers the best of everything. Ask for Part No. 95071. The upright Sump Witch™. is Part No. 95051. Both are problem-solvers. They're available at leading hardwares and home centers.

4.

8.

6. *Lower the Sump Witch™ into its crock, resting it level on the crock bottom so that the switch is farthest from the sump wall. Properly positioned, the discharge pipe comes up in the center of the crock.*

7. *Make the proper cutouts in the crock's safety cover for discharge piping and the upright pump's column. Blind impressions in the Polycrock cover indicate the locations and ease cutting.*

8. *The split cover now can be installed around the pump. If a submersible sump pump is used, make only one cutout in the cover for the discharge pipe. Motor and switch cords use the discharge opening.*

9. *A Genova Check Valve™ threads into the base module's discharge outlet using Teflon™ tape or silicone sealant on the threads. Stepped check valve permits connection to various sized discharge pipes.*

10. *Discharge piping can be run from the check valve to a convenient location where sump water can be drained. Rigid 1½" PVC piping is preferred for this because it will not interfere with the switch.*

11. *Final step is to plug the motor lead into the piggyback receptacle of the switch lead. Be sure that the outlet is a three-prong grounding type. If not, have one installed. A sump pump must be grounded.*

1. *Cut inlet openings in the side of the Polycrock for below-floor drainage pipes that will bring water to the sump. Make the holes slightly larger than the entering pipes using a small saw or knife.*

2. *Now the sump crock may be lowered into the hole made for it. The hole should be just deep enough to support the crock at or near floor level. Its bottom should be level. Crock holds 18 gallons.*

3. *Pour a soupy mix of portland cement, sand and water into the void around the Polycrock to both back it up and seal around the entering pipes. Water in the crock will keep it from floating.*

4. *Inlet pipes through the crock wall serve floor and footing drains and a basement laundry. More floor chipping may be necessary to install them.*

5. *Ragged edge around the chipped floor opening is filled with concrete patching compound. Trowel it out as neatly as you can. It will dry to a close match with the surrounding floor concrete.*

Plumb in an Automatic Washer

If you live in an older house without provision for an automatic washing machine, you can add it. The job couldn't be easier than with Genova PVC drain-waste-vent pipe and CPVC or PB water supply tubing.

Select a washer location convenient to a vent stack or building drain where you can pipe the waste water from the washer. Give second consideration to nearness to a point where you can tap a hot and cold water supply. You must also consider what floor space is available. An upstairs location may prove step-saving and it has the advantage that water can drain away by gravity. On the other hand, a basement location often is selected because the space is there.

In a basement laundry, unless your sewer exits below the basement floor level, waste water must be pumped out. Not many public health codes will permit the use of a sump pump for this, even though that's the way it's often done. While an ordinary sump pump system will handle laundry wastes all right, bacterial action takes place in the sump pit sometimes making for a smelly basement. Moreover, a periodic sump cleaning becomes a nasty job. The proper way to pump out laundry wastes from a basement is with a sewage ejector.

CONNECTING A DRAIN

Since an automatic washer's drain pipe is least flexible, make that run first. You may wish to add a laundry tray at the same time you plumb in the washer. It must be connected to a drain and vented the same as a kitchen sink.

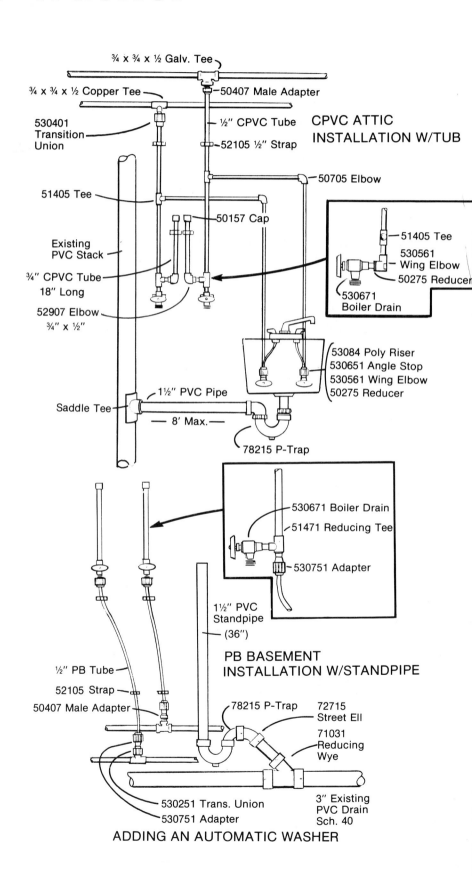

¾ x ¾ x ½ Galv. Tee
¾ x ¾ x ½ Copper Tee
530401 Transition Union
51405 Tee
Existing PVC Stack
¾" CPVC Tube 18" Long
52907 Elbow ¾" x ½"
Saddle Tee
50407 Male Adapter
½" CPVC Tube
52105 ½" Strap
50705 Elbow
50157 Cap

CPVC ATTIC INSTALLATION W/TUB

51405 Tee
530561 Wing Elbow
50275 Reducer
530671 Boiler Drain

53084 Poly Riser
530651 Angle Stop
530561 Wing Elbow
50275 Reducer

1½" PVC Pipe
8' Max.
78215 P-Trap

530671 Boiler Drain
51471 Reducing Tee
530751 Adapter

1½" PVC Standpipe (36")

PB BASEMENT INSTALLATION W/STANDPIPE

½" PB Tube
52105 Strap
50407 Male Adapter
530251 Trans. Union
530751 Adapter
78215 P-Trap
72715 Street Ell
71031 Reducing Wye
3" Existing PVC Drain Sch. 40

ADDING AN AUTOMATIC WASHER

Use a 1½-inch PVC waste pipe and vent. A laundry tray permits the use of a suds-saving automatic washer. In any case, the washer empties into the tub.

You can also drain a washer directly into what is called a standpipe, an 1½-inch PVC pipe reaching about 36 inches above the floor and located behind or beside the washer. A P-trap below the floor seals off the DWV system's gases from the house. With a standpipe, a suds-saving washer cannot be used effectively because there is nowhere to store the suds.

The same rules that apply to other wet-vented traps hold for the standpipe and laundry tray trap. If the distance is too far to a vent, the trap must be revented.

The washer's drain pipe can tie into a vent stack using a tee. Tie into a horizontal drain by dropping in from above via a 45-degree elbow and a wye inserted in the horizontal pipe. One drawing shows the use of a Part No. 61231 saddle tee. If your vent stack is a 3-inch Genova In-Wall Schedule 30 one, this easy method may be employed. In any case, the fittings you use to make the connection depend on what kind of pipes you are connecting to.

Water supply. A pair of ½-inch CPVC or PB hot and cold water pipes are run to the wall behind the washer. This is probably an ideal use for PB's flexibility. Either way, the system should end in a pair of threaded hose bibbs. Ahead of them you'll need two extra large air chambers made of ¾-inch CPVC tubes 18 inches long and capped at the top. These oversized chambers prevent damage to the water supply system when fast-acting washer solenoid valves snap shut after a fill cycle.

The drawings show the components of a CPVC and a PB system with two types of drain hookups. They are guides to

the parts you will need for your hookup. A basement system would be most similar to the attic-type hookup, which is supplied with water from above.

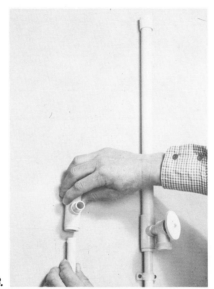
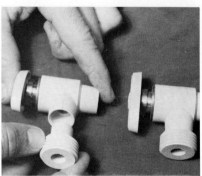

1. *The neatest, fastest way to make a hole in the floor for the washer's standpipe is with a hole saw. Chucked in an electric drill, this one cuts a 2" hole, clean as you please. (Other sizes are available.)*

2. *Drain hose from the washer slips inside the PVC standpipe and discharges waste washer water to the house drainage system. To keep system gases from escaping, a P-trap is installed below the floor.*

3. *Behind the washer supplies for hot and cold water are solvent welded of CPVC tube and fittings. A pair of ¾" x ¾" x ½" reducing tees with reducing bushings permit ½" supply tubes, ¾" air chambers.*

4. *Lacking Genova Part No. 530671 boiler drain valves for washer supply hose attachment, you can make them from Part No. 530661 ½" angle stop valves and Part No. 531281 male hose adapters solvent welded in.*

Plumbing a Half Bath

A half bath comprises a toilet and a lavatory. The end of a hallway or a closet provide enough space for an add-on, half bath, so does the corner of a large bedroom. The nearer you place it to existing drainage lines and hot and cold water supply lines the easier your plumbing job will be. A space as small as 2½ by 4 feet will do, but that's really tight. It's better to have more.

Draw out a floor plan of your fixture arrangement before you start hacking up walls and floors. Plan for the toilet first; then plan the lavatory to fit. Tiny lavatories as small as a foot square can be had, but the more normal sized ones stick out from the wall at least 1½ feet and are that wide or wider.

Add a door and window(s) to your half bath layout. If no window is available, you can meet codes by installing a vent fan. This may vent through the bath's wall or ceiling. Final discharge may be through the house wall or roof, ducting and discharge vent are available where you get the fan unit. Some vent fans incorporate a bathroom light along with the fan. Get whatever kind you like best.

Some plumbing codes permit no windows and no vent fan if you use a toilet that power vents the bowl through the DWV system. It works by water action. Check your code.

1. A half bath can be built in a very small space. A cabinet-type lavatory with a separate china top helps solve the storage problem without using additional space.

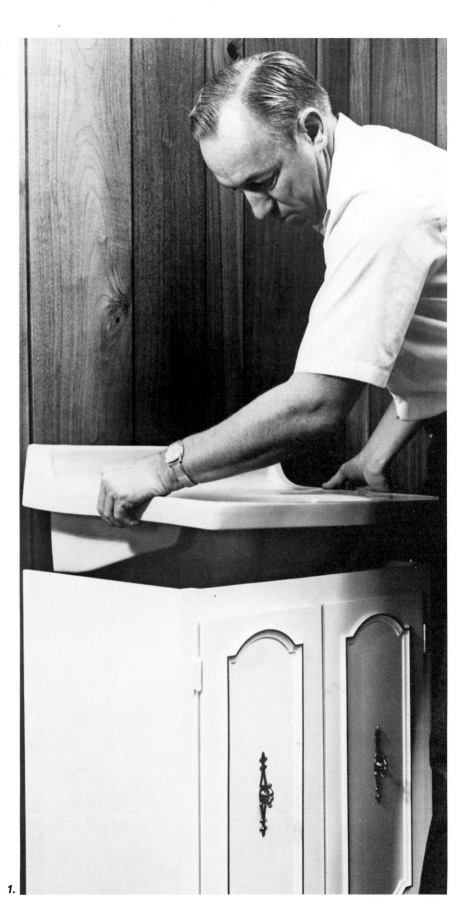

1.

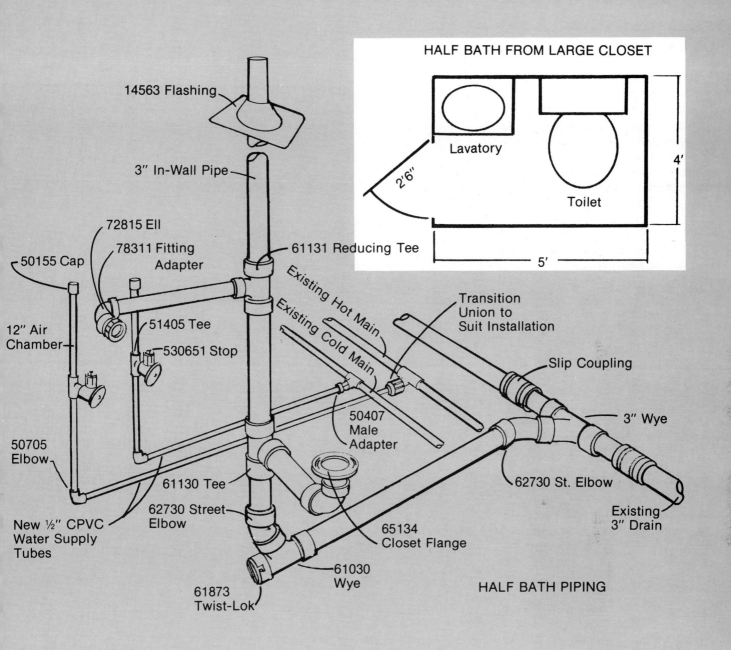

14563 Flashing

3" In-Wall Pipe

72815 Ell

78311 Fitting Adapter

50155 Cap

61131 Reducing Tee

12" Air Chamber

51405 Tee

530651 Stop

Existing Hot Main

Existing Cold Main

Transition Union to Suit Installation

Slip Coupling

50407 Male Adapter

3" Wye

50705 Elbow

61130 Tee

62730 Street Elbow

62730 St. Elbow

Existing 3" Drain

New ½" CPVC Water Supply Tubes

65134 Closet Flange

61030 Wye

61873 Twist-Lok

HALF BATH PIPING

HALF BATH FROM LARGE CLOSET

Lavatory

2'6"

Toilet

4'

5'

Existing or new stack? Whether you connect your new bathroom fixtures to a main vent that's already there or run a new vent up through the roof depends on how far away the present one is. We don't advise locating the new toilet any farther than eight feet from the 3- or 4-inch existing main vent stack. The distance is that measured along the centerline of the toilet waste pipes and fittings.

In many cases installing a new vent up through the roof is the easiest method.

In any case, toilet and lavatory wastes will drain by gravity into the existing building drain. Make the new-to-old drain connection with a wye and slip couplings or no-hub joints, as show on pages 45 and 75. Remember that the flow must always enter a drain in the same direction as the flow already in it. Entry

from above is desirable, although side entry is permissible.

Avoid right angle turns in drains, except through special long sweep elbows, and be sure to provide cleanouts for all horizontal runs of pipe that are not accessible for cleaning from the fixture location. Genova Twist-Lok™ cleanouts are ideal for this.

If wet-venting is not permitted by your code, the lavatory will have to be provided with both a drain and a vent. The chapter on DWV piping and the one on plumbing for a whole house or addition both contain helpful information on piping for an add-on bath.

Bringing in the water supply to both fixtures is the simplest part of the job. For that we recommend use of a plumbing manifold, which is featured beginning on page 30.

The accompanying pictures show steps involved in adding a half bath with new through-the-roof venting. The wide selection of Genova pipes and fittings is your best friend when it comes to adding a half bathroom. Sketch out both your DWV and water supply piping arrangement and order the necessary pipes and fittings from your Genova dealer. He will be pleased to help you in choosing the right ones for the job.

1.

2.

3.

1. Plumb the DWV system for your add-on bath using a 3" Genova In-Wall vent stack. No furring out of walls is required. Mark around a cut-off piece of pipe for holes to be made for the vent pipe.

2. The hole can be cut with a proper-sized hole saw or, lacking that, by drilling a series of smaller holes centered on the circle. These should almost touch each other. Don't drill into wiring.

3. Then saw out between holes with a keyhole saw. A chisel will work, too. The wood plug will drop out, leaving an opening large enough to pass the pipe with a little clearance to spare.

4.

5.

6.

4. Use a plumb bob to transfer hole locations from top to bottom or bottom to top so that vent pipes run vertically. The vent stack should be positioned as close to the toilet as you can get it.

5. With the hole for the vent stack cut in the floor, cut through the ceiling and up into the attic. Before drilling, always check to see what's on the other side. You may not want to bore into it. Wear eye protection when drilling.

6. If the add-on bath is located away from an existing vent stack, it will have to have its own vent and a below-floor connection to a building drain. Begin by cutting out the drain pipe for the connection.

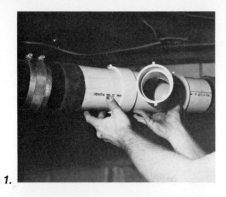

1.

2.

3.

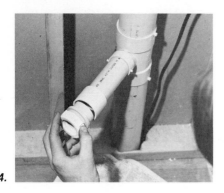

4.

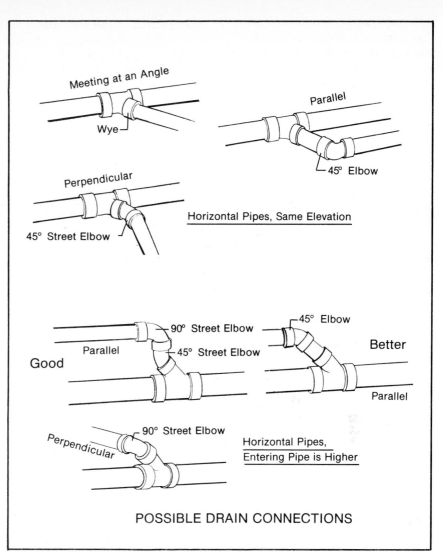

Meeting at an Angle

Wye

Parallel

45° Elbow

Perpendicular

45° Street Elbow

Horizontal Pipes, Same Elevation

90° Street Elbow

Parallel

45° Street Elbow

Good

45° Elbow

Better

Parallel

90° Street Elbow

Perpendicular

Horizontal Pipes,
Entering Pipe is Higher

POSSIBLE DRAIN CONNECTIONS

1. One method of joining new and old drain pipes uses No-Hub neoprene rubber sleeves and clamps. Insert solvent welded add-on wye into the cut-out line. No-Hub joints have been slipped over pipe ends.

2. Now slide the No-Hub joints astride the old and new pipes, first the sleeves, then the clamps. Tighten the clamps and you're done. Exposed wye accepts an add-on drain connection.

3. From a Genova special waste and vent fitting or drainage tee below the floor bring up the new vent stack. If the lavatory is near enough, drain it directly into the vent by inserting a reducing tee.

4. Trap adapter solvent welds to the end of the lavatory waste run. This one required a coupling. Another version fits the 1½" pipe directly. Angled waste pipe aims toward center of the lavatory drain.

Plumbing a Half Bath **75**

1. These Genova Snap-Fit™ Roof Flashings provide a permanent seal around plumbing vent pipe and electrical masts.

2. Vent run continues through the attic and out the roof. An offset, made of a pair of 45° elbows solvent welded to the stack with a length of 3" pipe between, made this vent miss a roof rafter.

3. The use of a plumb bob ensures that the final vent run out through the roof is vertical. With the bob centered in the pipe fitting below, the string at the top shows the center of the hole in the roof.

4. If you drive a nail vertically through the roof boards and roofing centered above the vent fitting, the protruding nail above will tell you where to make the cutout. Cut from above or below.

1.

2.

3.

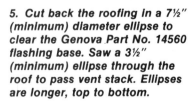

4.

5.

5. Cut back the roofing in a 7½" (minimum) diameter ellipse to clear the Genova Part No. 14560 flashing base. Saw a 3½" (minimum) ellipse through the roof to pass vent stack. Ellipses are longer, top to bottom.

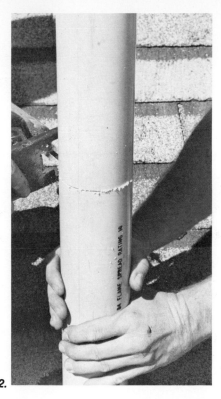

1.

2.

3.

4.

1. The final length of vent pipe is inserted from above and solvent welded from inside the attic by a helper. Then it may be cut off a foot above the roof. Be sure to measure from the high side.

2. After giving the final solvent welded joint an hour to set, you can saw off the vent pipe as marked. You may make the cut right away if you're careful not to twist or cock the pipe as you cut it.

3. Install a Genova Snap-Fit™ thermoplastic weatherproof roof flashing base underneath the roofing with the shingles over-lapping it at least half way down. Slip a 3″ collar on.

4. The completed flashing with collar snapped down around the base is not only leak-free, it never needs painting and will not stain the roof. Flashing can be used on all types of vent pipe.

1. *An easy method of adapting CPVC to copper water lines is with a Genova universal adapter. A stainless steel grab-ring and a neoprene O-ring form both a mechanical and a hydraulic seal.*

2. *To adapt CPVC pipe to threaded hot water fittings, use a threaded transition fitting.*

3. *To adapt CPVC to cold water mains, a CPVC male adapter is used.*

4. *Holes for water supply pipes are easily drilled using a high speed wood bit in an electric drill. Make the holes slightly larger than the outside diameter of the pipes you're using.*

5. *Flexible polybutylene tubing can be threaded through walls, floors and ceilings as easily as electrical cables are. Fittings are needed only at the ends of runs. These are made of CPVC.*

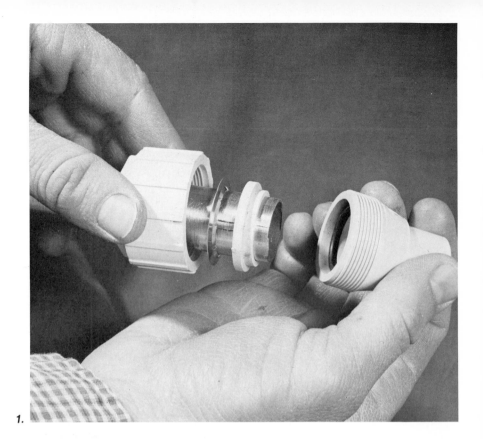

1.

2.

3.

4.

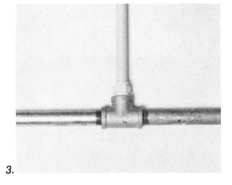

5.

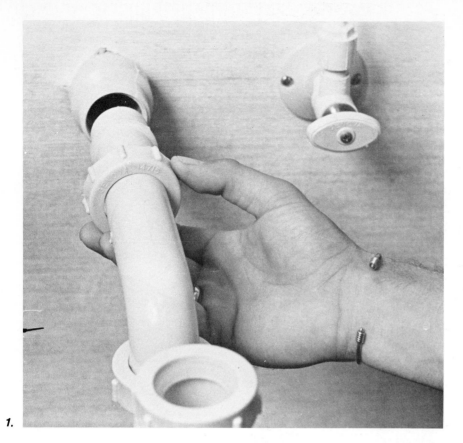

1.

1. The trap arm of Genova polypropylene P-trap slips into a trap adapter at the wall. The trap's slip nut and poly ring should be installed over the trap arm. Poly ring wedge aims toward the trap adapter. The trap is sealed at the wall by tightening the slip nut onto the threaded trap adapter. Wall stub-outs for lavatories and sinks should end in trap adapters, also called Marvel couplings.

2. For connecting a toilet, solvent weld a Genova closet flange to the below-floor toilet waste pipe. First coat the pipe with solvent. The floor hole should be 5″ to clear the shoulder of the flange.

3. Next coat the inside of the PVC closet flange fitting with solvent, being very generous with it as usual. Note that the flashed-over closet flange opening is still intact to keep the DWV system clean.

4. Immediately push the closet flange onto the end of the pipe with a slight twist, just as for installing a solvent welded pipe and fitting. Get the bolt slots aligned on either side of the toilet. (Genova also makes a closet flange with an adjustable bolt ring which assures easy alignment.)

5. Toilet bowl is lowered onto the closet flange, after removing its flashed-over opening and installing a wax toilet bowl gasket over the outlet horn. (See how to do this in another chapter.)

2.

3.

4.

5.

Plumbing for a Whole House or Addition

When you take on the plumbing for a new house, vacation home or home addition, you become a real plumber. Actually, though, new work is easier than remodeling or add-on plumbing because everything is accessible. Finished wall, floor and ceiling materials haven't yet been put in, so you can work pretty much unobstructed.

New plumbing should be done in two stages: rough and finished. The time to do the rough plumbing is after the house has been closed in to weather, but before any insulation or inside finish materials have been installed. Ideally, roof flashings have been placed under the finished roofing material before that was put on. And, in the case of a concrete slab house, all under slab plumbing should have been roughed in before the slab was poured. Of course, sleeves through the foundation should have been provided for the water supply service pipe and the building drain.

Finished plumbing consists of fixture installation. It is done after the wall, floor and inside ceiling materials have been installed and finished. Finished plumbing is one of the last steps to completing the house.

The first step in plumbing a house or addition is to plan it. Make rough sketches. Very rough is all right, just so you understand them. A good deal of the plans may even be in your head.

Planning for the water supply system starts where the utility stops. This may be at an outdoor service entrance shutoff valve, or it may be at the water meter. If you have your own water system, it probably starts at the pump.

Installation of the water supply system should come after that of the DWV system because its. smaller pipes are easier to work in among the larger ones.

DWV planning. To build a good operating DWV system, you need proper pipe sizing. Pipes too small will not carry the flow. Pipes too large are "lazy" and tend to clog. To get the right size, consult Tables A and B. These deal with fixture units. A fixture unit, which is the basis for DWV pipe sizing, has a waste flow of about one cubic foot a minute (about 7½ gallons). It's the accepted measuring stick for waste plumbing design.

First, size the toilet drain pipe and the waste pipes for each fixture according to these rules of thumb: toilet - 3-inch; shower - 2-inch; bathtub only, kitchen sink, laundry, floor drain, lavatory - 1½-inch.

Then size drain pipes that collect the wastes from more than one fixture. Using Table A, add up the fixture units for the groups of fixtures that will use a collective drain. Then see what pipe size in Table B will handle it. For example, if a bathtub, a lavatory and a kitchen sink all will use the same horizontal drain pipe, that makes a total of five fixture units (from Table A). The horizontal drain pipe necessary to handle five fixture units is 2-inch (from Table B).

DESIGN OF DWV SYSTEM
(National Plumbing Code)

Table A			Table B	
				Fixture Units Permissible
Fixtures	Fixture Units	Pipe Size	Horizontal Pipe	Vertical Pipe
Toilet	4	1½"	3	8
Bathtub/Shower	2	2"	6*	16
Shower	2	3"	20**	30***
Sink	2	4"	160	240
Lavatory	1			
Laundry Tray	2			
Floor Drain	1	*waste only		
One 3-pc. Bathroom group: toilet, tub lavatory	6	**not more than two toilets on horizontal line		
		***not more than six toilets on one stack		

Next, size the main stack. If only two toilets, plus other smaller fixtures drain into it, a 3-inch stack should do easily, but check the tables anyway. Stacks, of course, are vertical pipes.

Finally, add up the fixture units for all house fixtures and figure how large the main building drain will have to be to carry off the collected wastes. You'll find, in most cases, that a 3-inch pipe will suffice. Building drains are mostly horizontal pipes.

Size all vents serving toilets at three inches. (Some codes permit 2-inch vents for toilets.) Try to arrange your drainage runs so the lavatory sink, bathtub and shower all empty into the main stack above the point where the toilet does. If they enter in the same fitting as the toilet, refer to the Tables. That way, you probably won't need separate vents for these fixtures. Any that connect below the toilet must be revented. Connect all revent lines into the handiest vent stack at least six inches above the flood rim of the highest fixture that drains into that stack.

A revent pipe should be the same size as the waste pipe for a fixture.

If a sink or lavatory is to be drained below the floor, it must be revented, otherwise its trap may be siphoned dry by the falling water.

In freezing climates vent runs that exit through the roof should be 3- or 4-inch to prevent icing over. Smaller runs can be increased in size at a point 12 inches below the roof using the appropriate Genova reducing couplings.

Plumbing for a house, vacation house or addition is little more than cutting the parts of the system--the pipes--to fit and assembling them to their fittings. Here CPVC is run to a water softener.

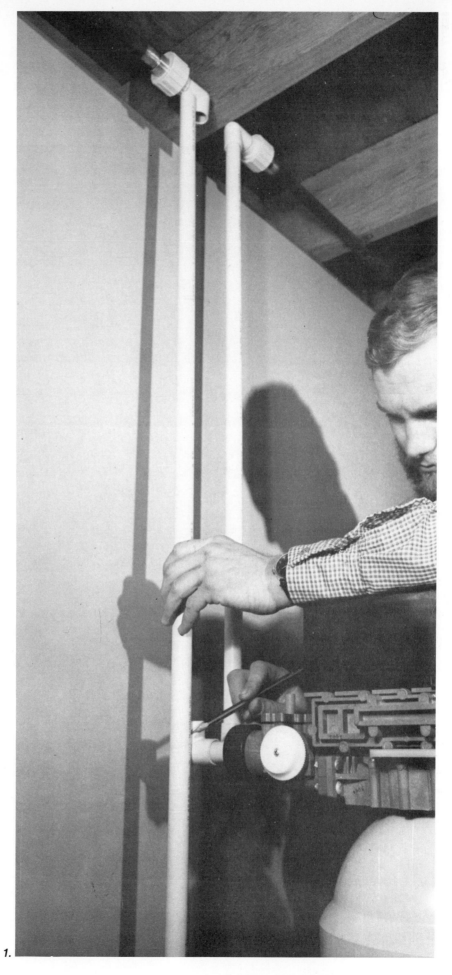

1.

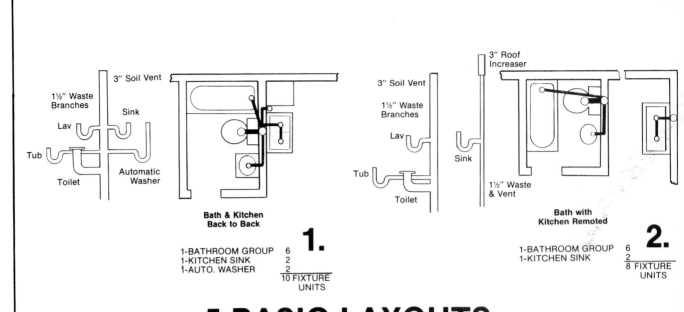

**Bath & Kitchen
Back to Back**

1-BATHROOM GROUP	6
1-KITCHEN SINK	2
1-AUTO. WASHER	2
	10 FIXTURE UNITS

1.

**Bath with
Kitchen Remoted**

1-BATHROOM GROUP	6
1-KITCHEN SINK	2
	8 FIXTURE UNITS

2.

5 BASIC LAYOUTS

Carry all vent stacks to a point 12 inches above the roof line at the exit point.

The sample bathroom layouts illustrated may give you ideas on piping arrangements. All are for compact plumbing setups using wet-venting.

Wet-vented runs more than eight feet long must be revented whether or not they drain above a toilet, and if you near the maximum length, be sure to keep the pipe slopes at ¼-inch per foot. The National Plumbing Code requires even shorter wet-vented maximums: 3-inch pipe - 5 feet; 2-inch pipe - 3½ feet; 1½-inch pipe - 2½ feet. This is "developed length," or the total length from trap weir to vent stack measured along the centerlines of pipe and fittings. A good rule of thumb if you are not saddled with restrictive codes, is keep all fixture drain lines to a maximum of eight feet from a vent pipe.

If your local code won't okay wet-venting, you'll have to install revent runs above each fixture trap. Your building inspector should be happy to explain what is required locally.

Drainage runs. Vent only piping may be connected using short turn tees, crosses or whatever fitting works best, whether it's a drainage-type fitting or not. Drain piping must use drainage-type fittings for unrestricted flow.

In addition, keep in mind a few simple rules about drainage piping to provide unrestricted flow of wastes by gravity.

Keep drain runs as straight as possible. Where you must bend them, use two 45-degree elbows rather than one 90-degree elbow, or use a long sweep 90-degree elbow.

An exception: It's all right to use a 90-degree elbow to dump waste from a horizontal pipe into a vertical one because the sudden drop forestalls any flow problems.

The opposite is not true. When changing from a vertical to a horizontal pipe, avoid using a regular 90-degree elbow or tee. Thus, never install a tee lying on its back, that is, with the flow making the 90-degree bend from vertical to horizontal. Use a wye and 45-degree elbow, which provides you with an opening for

a cleanout instead. A tee should be used only where the flow is from horizontal to vertical.

Moreover, never use an ordinary tee to connect one horizontal drainage pipe to another. The sharp turn disrupts the flow too drastically. Instead, use a wye placed so that incoming wastes enter in the direction of flow. If the two pipes meet at right angles, a 45-degree elbow plus a wye does the trick.

If the entering pipe is higher than the one being entered, you can drop in from above using a 90- or 45-degree elbow and a wye together. Which elbow you use depends on whether the pipes are parallel (45-degree) or perpendicular (90-degree). (See drawing on page 75.)

It's a good idea to limit horizontal fixture waste runs to a total horizontal turn of 90 degrees between the trap and the stack or drain. Doing it takes planning. Sink and lavatory waste pipes may exit the room at an angle to the wall. This sometimes lets them be run directly into a stack without any bends.

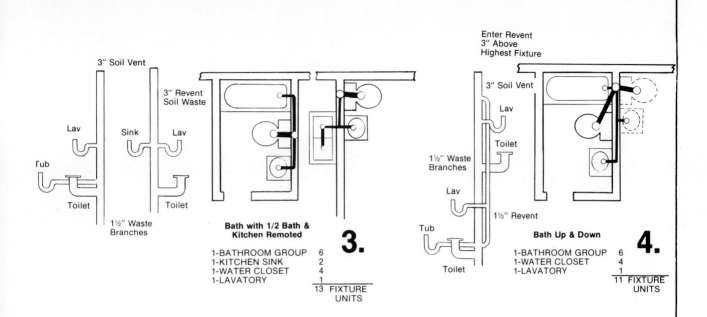

**Bath with 1/2 Bath &
Kitchen Remoted**

1-BATHROOM GROUP	6
1-KITCHEN SINK	2
1-WATER CLOSET	4
1-LAVATORY	1
	13 FIXTURE UNITS

3.

Enter Revent
3" Above
Highest Fixture

Bath Up & Down

1-BATHROOM GROUP	6
1-WATER CLOSET	4
1-LAVATORY	1
	11 FIXTURE UNITS

4.

Or, the use of a 45-degree elbow in the wall behind a lavatory or sink lets the waste pipe enter the wall at an angle, yet turn toward the nearest stack to the right or left. In any case, entry to the stack may be through a 3 x 3 x 1½-inch reducing tee. Drawings on page 87 illustrate these methods.

Pipe stubout arrangements, called rough-ins, should be handled as shown on page 91. Then you can be sure that all traps and riser tubes will fit up.

Waste-vent fitting. Behind and beneath every toilet is either a waste and vent tee or a Genova special waste and vent fitting. The special fitting, made only by Genova, enables you to completely customize an installation. Unless a toilet is the ONLY fixture to be drained and vented below the floor at that point, we recommend using the special waste and vent fitting. It's available in 3 x 2- and 3⁻1½-inch. The larger size can serve both 2- and 1½-inch waste pipes by using reducers for the 1½-inch pipes. There's even a special waste and vent fitting made for two bathrooms back-to-back, which

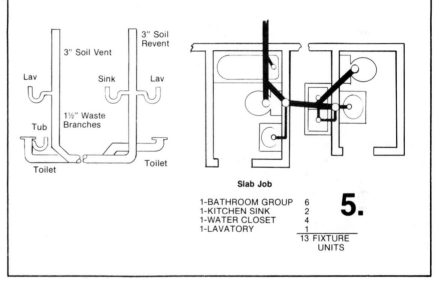

Slab Job

1-BATHROOM GROUP	6
1-KITCHEN SINK	2
1-WATER CLOSET	4
1-LAVATORY	1
	13 FIXTURE UNITS

5.

is a good way to arrange them. Top caps for all these fittings are provided, which contain a single socket for a 3-inch vent stack or have as many as two additional vents or drains in 1½-inch or sometimes 2-inch.

Any unused side opening in a special waste and vent fitting may be plugged. One plug comes with every fitting.

RUNNING DWV

When you have all your pipes and fittings on hand, you're ready to begin assembling the house plumbing system. Start with the DWV portion. Begin it beneath the floor behind the toilet with the waste and vent fitting (or tee). Place this key part with its smoothly curved passage arranged in the direction of water flow. Holding it in position centered below the wall behind the toilet, mark the necessary 3½-inch hole for the vent run. Also, cut out a 5-inch hole in the bathroom floor for the toilet flange. If a framing member is in the way of a toilet waste run, you may remove part of the member by installing a header across to support what's left of it between the two flanking members.

Now you're ready to run 3-inch waste and vent pipes in all three directions from the waste and vent fitting. The chapter on adding a bathroom shows plumbing steps that also apply to new construction.

Pipes may be run parallel with framing members, no problem. Support them on headers nailed between members. When running them across the framing, the members must be notched. Avoid that as much as you can. Basement and crawl-space cross-member framing runs can be installed without notching.

When you make the drainage run, be sure to install a cleanout at the high end of every horizontal run. It's made using a wye with a Twist-Lok™ cleanout fitting, such as Part No. 61873, installed in the open end.

Also, be sure to install other wyes carefully positioned to accommodate entering drains from other stacks.

If you need to offset a drainage run to clear an obstruction, use two 45-degree elbows. Offsets in vent-only runs

1.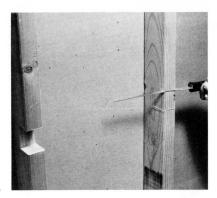

2.

3.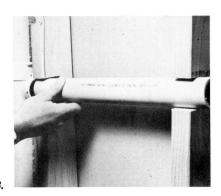

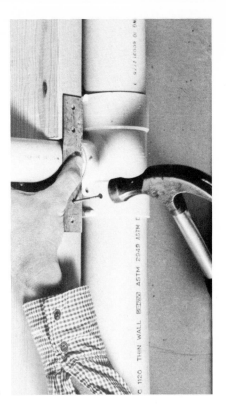

4.

may be made with 90-degree elbows. If one elbow is a street elbow, no short pipe will be needed to join them.

Slope and support drain runs, as described in another chapter. Any notching of house framing should be done according to the rules of good notching shown in the accompanying drawing.

In running up a vent stack, install any necessary tees for entering waste and vent runs as you go. Those for vent runs may be vent tees such as Part No. 61430 or else drainage tees installed upside down. Never use a vent tee for drainage purposes, though.

1. Wall framing is notched to pass horizontal drain and vent pipes. To do it, saw in on both sides full depth of the notch. Don't notch any deeper than 2¼" or you'll overly weaken the wall.

2. Then take out the wood plug you've created with a sharp chisel, placing the chisel at the bottom of the notch and tapping it with a hammer. If you don't have an all-metal plumber's chisel, use a shop-type, being gentle. Wear goggles when chiseling.

3. The horizontal pipe can then be solvent welded in place. This one was a drain pipe for a lavatory, permitting it to waste above the floor into the 3" vent stack via a reducing tee placed in the stack.

4. Notches should be reinforced and piping protected by nailing steel straps across the notched out studs. Made ⅛" thick, the punched straps are available where builder's hardware is sold.

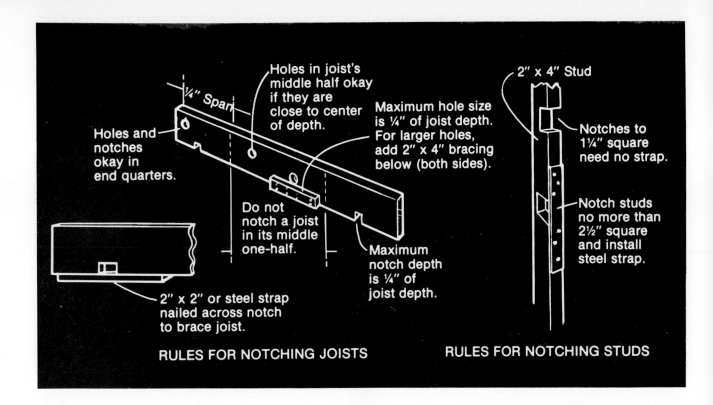

Holes and notches okay in end quarters.

¼" Span

Holes in joist's middle half okay if they are close to center of depth.

Maximum hole size is ¼" of joist depth. For larger holes, add 2" x 4" bracing below (both sides).

Do not notch a joist in its middle one-half.

Maximum notch depth is ¼" of joist depth.

2" x 2" or steel strap nailed across notch to brace joist.

RULES FOR NOTCHING JOISTS

2" x 4" Stud

Notches to 1¼" square need no strap.

Notch studs no more than 2½" square and install steel strap.

RULES FOR NOTCHING STUDS

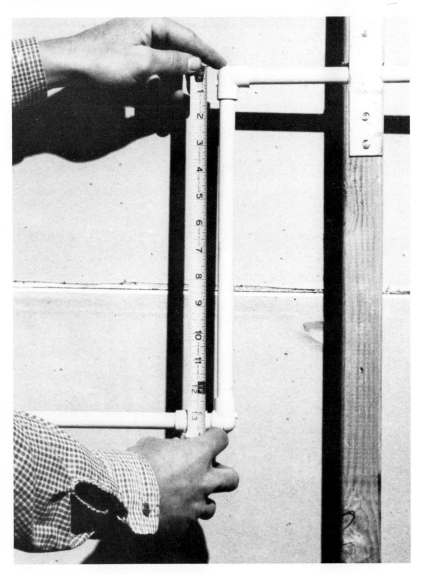

1.

1. Long, straight runs of water supply and DWV piping should contain offsets to permit thermal expansion and contraction. Doglegs about 12" long made with 90° elbows do the job for a water line.

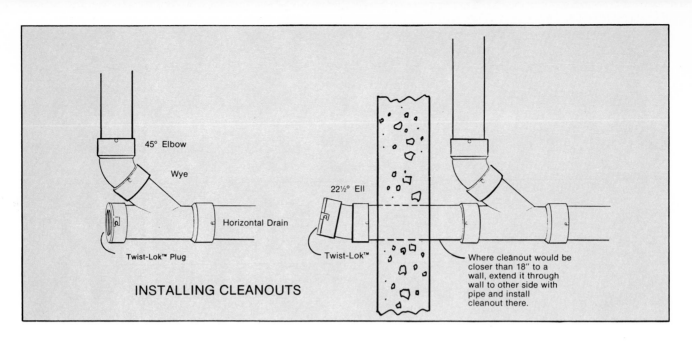

INSTALLING CLEANOUTS

45° Elbow

Wye

Horizontal Drain

Twist-Lok™ Plug

22½° Ell

Twist-Lok™

Where cleanout would be closer than 18" to a wall, extend it through wall to other side with pipe and install cleanout there.

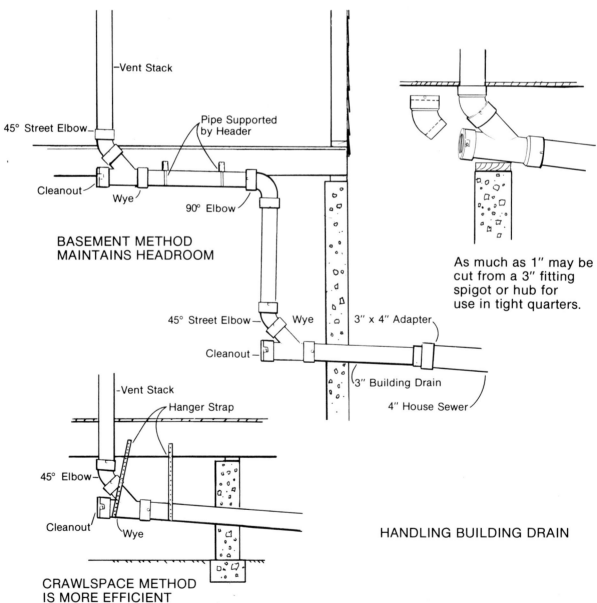

-Vent Stack

45° Street Elbow

Pipe Supported by Header

Cleanout

Wye

90° Elbow

BASEMENT METHOD MAINTAINS HEADROOM

45° Street Elbow

Wye

Cleanout

3" x 4" Adapter

3" Building Drain

4" House Sewer

As much as 1" may be cut from a 3" fitting spigot or hub for use in tight quarters.

-Vent Stack

Hanger Strap

45° Elbow

Cleanout

Wye

HANDLING BUILDING DRAIN

CRAWLSPACE METHOD IS MORE EFFICIENT

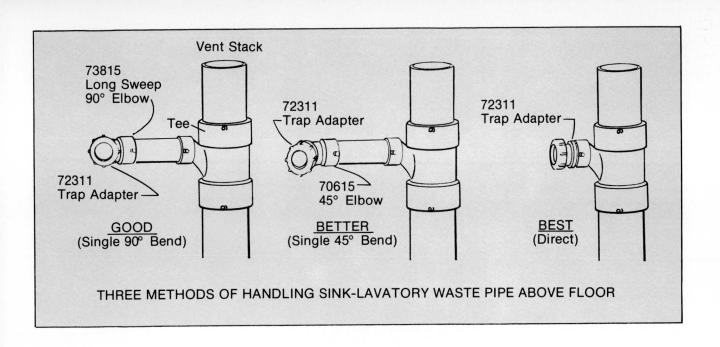

THREE METHODS OF HANDLING SINK-LAVATORY WASTE PIPE ABOVE FLOOR

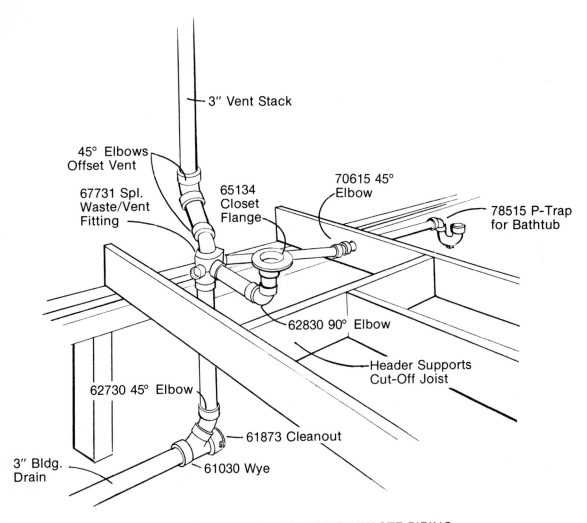

BOXING OUT FRAMING FOR TOILET WASTE PIPING

Carry vent stacks out through the roof, installing a Genova Snap-Fit™ thermoplastic flashing to keep out rain water.

Add enough to pipe lengths before cutting to allow them to fully enter their fitting sockets (see table on makeup). If in doubt, take measurements right on the fitting. Subtract for the distance taken up by any fitting that's included in a measurement. You can cut all pipes and dry assemble them with their fittings to make sure everything fits. Finally, take your dry assembly apart, solvent welding the joints.

Smaller waste pipes are installed after the larger 3-inchers go in. Work from what's already installed back to the fixtures. Install a 1½-inch PVC P-trap for a bathtub, such as Part No. 78415 or Part No. 176151, and a 2-incher for shower-only, such as Part No. 78420.

Revent runs, if used, are carried up from fixtures via tees and elbowed over to enter a vent stack through a tee. Revent connections may be made in the attic, if desired. Revent runs may include 90-degree bends in the form of elbows and tees. Vent air flow is not restricted.

If it's easier to revent out through the roof, then do so.

Testing DWV. When you finish your roughed-in DWV system, you'll want to water-test it. Plug openings at the toilet (a Genova Pop-Top™ closet flange already takes care of this) and at all trap adapters including lavatory, sink, tub/shower. Don't forget to plug the lower end of the building drain. You can make temporary plugs out of mortar stuffed into the pipes against wadded-up newspapers. Let the plugs harden overnight, then fill the whole DWV system with water through a garden hose placed in the roof vent. If the level holds, and you can find no leaks, you're home free. The plugs can be removed by chiseling (don't make them very thick).

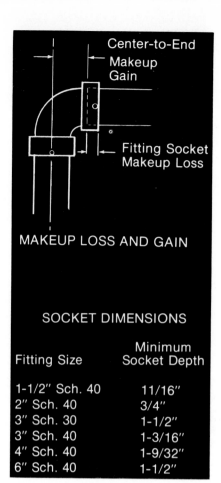

MAKEUP LOSS AND GAIN

SOCKET DIMENSIONS

Fitting Size	Minimum Socket Depth
1-1/2″ Sch. 40	11/16″
2″ Sch. 40	3/4″
3″ Sch. 30	1-1/2″
3″ Sch. 40	1-3/16″
4″ Sch. 40	1-9/32″
6″ Sch. 40	1-1/2″

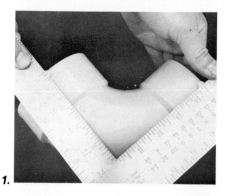

1.

2.

1. When transferring house measurements to pipe, always allow for fitting makeup. Pipes turning a corner do not reach into the corner but stop short inside the fitting. Square shows how much.

2. The square-test will show you how much a toilet waste pipe should reach short of the finished floor by measuring against a closet flange. Don't forget that the pipe must also reach about 1½″ into the socket.

1.

2.

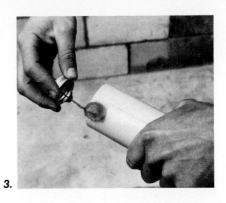

3.

4.

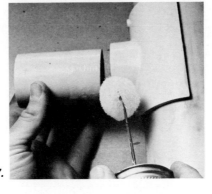

7.

7. The added-on drain or vent run may then be solvent welded right into the saddle tee's socket. While not all plumbing codes approve it, a saddle tee can be a lifesaver in new or old plumbing.

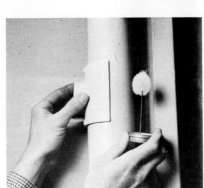

5.

6.

1. When you start a plumbing project, set aside a work area near where your materials and tools are. A vertical 2" x 4" block clamped to a sawhorse lets it be used for sawing pipes off the floor.

2. For really square cuts in DWV and water supply pipes, use a miter box. You can make or buy it. Complete details of making successful solvent welded joints are given in other chapters.

3. Before you begin the solvent welding process, stop and think for a few seconds. Mistakes mean spoiled joints that must be cut out and replaced. Once you apply the solvent, you're well committed.

4. If you forget to install a 1½" reducing tee in a 3" vent stack, Genova makes a solvent welded saddle tee that can save the day. It's also great for tapping into an existing 3" stack.

5. Once both the side of the pipe and the saddle tee fitting have been coated generously with solvent, press the tee firmly onto the stack and hold it there for 10 seconds while the solvent firms up.

6. Then drill out the stack to the same diameter as the saddle tee opening, being careful not to damage the fitting socket. A round or half-round file will remove any material the drill can't get.

1.

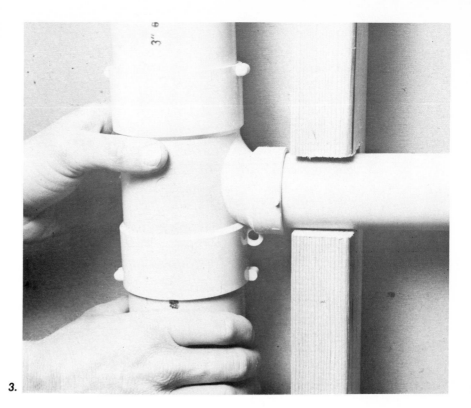

2.

3.

1. Make up a shower drain with a standard waste connection by packing rope oakum tightly around the 2″ PVC pipe. Leave 1″ of pipe exposed above the oakum for filling with Plastic Lead Seal.

2. Underside of the shower drain shows how the 2″ PVC pipe enters a 2″ Part No. 78420 P-trap with cleanout, then leads toward a convenient drain. Length of such a wet-vent is limited (see text).

3. Vent runs entering a stack via a reducing tee may be made either with a special vent tee or by using a standard sanitary tee upside down (as shown). This lets gases escape upward into the vent.

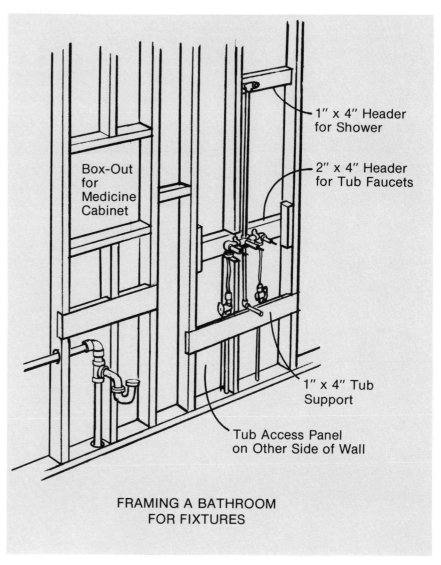

Box-Out for Medicine Cabinet

1″ x 4″ Header for Shower

2″ x 4″ Header for Tub Faucets

1″ x 4″ Tub Support

Tub Access Panel on Other Side of Wall

FRAMING A BATHROOM FOR FIXTURES

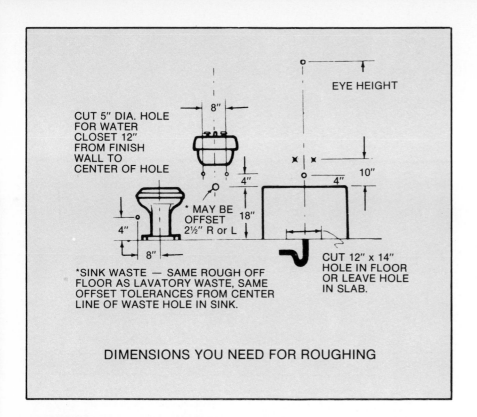

CUT 5" DIA. HOLE FOR WATER CLOSET 12" FROM FINISH WALL TO CENTER OF HOLE

8"

EYE HEIGHT

10"

4"

4"

18"

* MAY BE OFFSET 2½" R or L

4"

8"

CUT 12" x 14" HOLE IN FLOOR OR LEAVE HOLE IN SLAB.

*SINK WASTE — SAME ROUGH OFF FLOOR AS LAVATORY WASTE, SAME OFFSET TOLERANCES FROM CENTER LINE OF WASTE HOLE IN SINK.

DIMENSIONS YOU NEED FOR ROUGHING

1.

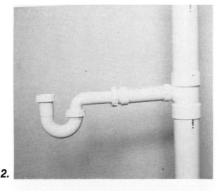

2.

3.

1. A toilet bowl bolts down with a pair of bolts attached to the closet flange at the floor. Tighten snugly, but not so tight that the bowl base is strained. Caps later cover the bolt ends.

2. & 3. A Genova Part No. 175151 lavatory/sink P-trap gives some latitude in fixture placement. Extended straight out, it has a long reach (2.). Pushed in swiveled, it works close to the wall (3.).

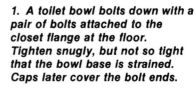

TUBE SIZES TO FIXTURES

MAXIMUM LENGTH OF RUN (ft.)

Pipe Size	Faucets Served		
	1	2	3
3/8"	25	--	--
1/2"	100+	20	--
3/4"	100+	100+	80

Installing the water supply. The final rough plumbing project is the water supply piping. It's routine, and directions for doing it have already been covered in other chapters. Maintain about six inches space between hot and cold water pipes. Be sure to make vertical supply runs to fixtures with the hot water pipe on the left as you face the fixture and the cold on the right.

Install valves, a main shutoff after the water meter and a shutoff on the cold water supply to the water heater. For these use Part No. 530151, ½/¾-inch CPVC line stops or if you want a stop-and-drain feature, use Part No. 530161. Also, install stop valves at every fixture in the hot and cold water supplies. Use either Part No. 530561, ½-inch CPVC x ⅜-inch PB angle stops, or Part No. 530301, straight stops. Use valves on entering any type of water-using appliance so you can still have water pressure even though the appliance is out for servicing.

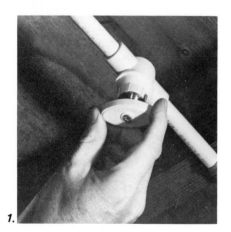

1.

As part of your water supply installation, cut header boards into the studs and nail them solidly behind the lavatory, sink, tub and shower. These, if not used to support a hanging fixture, will be used to brace the water supply piping. Get them at the correct height to do the job. It's best, though not necessary, to have the plumbing fixtures on hand when you do the rough plumbing.

Testing the water supply. Water-test the supply system by having every supply outlet either temporarily capped or valved off. Then turn on the water at the house main, bleed off air by opening the highest faucet and look for leaks. If there are none after 12 hours, you're done. Any leaks in a CPVC system can be repaired by draining the system, sawing out the affected joint and solvent welding a new one in. Use couplings to connect it. Leaking PB joints may only need refitting.

With both water supply system and DWV system leak-checked and inspected if need be, you're ready to insulate and close in the walls. Fixture installation, which follows that, has been covered in another chapter.

The planning and work you do in plumbing your house or addition will have saved you at least as much as what you've spent for plumbing materials and fixtures, because these are usually less than half the cost. In any case, it should have been well worth your while, for plumbing is one of the most enjoyable parts of house building. It's merely a matter of cutting and fitting the parts, and no parts cut or fit easier than those by Genova. They've been designed with that in mind.

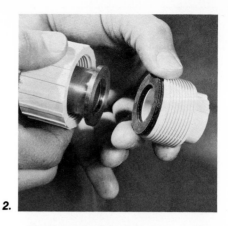

2.

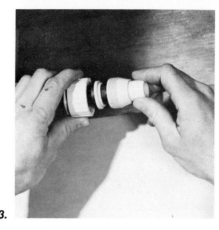

3.

1. For full water control, your supply system should contain several shutoff valves: one main shutoff, one at the cold water entry to the water heater and one placed at any water-using appliance.

2. For a house addition, you may need to adapt a new vinyl water supply system to an existing one of some other type. Do it with a Genova transition adapter, this one for sweat copper to CPVC.

3. This Genova universal adapter lets you connect CPVC to sweat copper tubing without soldering. It pushes on and tightens around the tubing watertight. It also works on CPVC tube, but not PB.

THAWING FROZEN PLASTIC PIPES

Extremely cold weather brings with it a high frequency of "how do we thaw frozen plastic pipe?" questions. This will acquaint you with a few of the methods which may be safely employed without damaging the system.

Remember that pipe freezing problems are usually the result of improper installation. This usually takes the form of underground pipes buried above the frost line or water pipes installed in unheated spaces and improperly insulated. Note that pipes exposed to repeated freezing conditions may rupture and the ultimate solution is to reinstall the piping, taking proper precautions against freezing temperatures.

The only safe way to thaw a plastic water pipe is with a pot of hot water and an old towel. The towel is dipped into the hot water, wrung dry, and held over the spot suspected of being frozen. Repeated applications may be necessary.

It's unnecessary to use extremely high temperatures in thawing the pipes since water freezes at 32° F and melts at 33° F.

A more practical method to thaw buried pipes is to disconnect an exposed end and insert a flexible plastic pipe of one half the pipe diameter or less. The inserted pipe should be sufficiently stiff to allow it to be pushed through the frozen pipe until the ice is encountered. Once this position is achieved, the other end of the small pipe is hooked to a hot water pressure source or fed via a funnel and tea kettle by gravity. The warm water should sufficiently dislodge the ice. Caution: If the frozen line is a pressure pipe, be sure to turn off the pressure source before attempting this thawing method for obvious reasons.

Never use an open flame to thaw plastic pipes. It's a fire hazard and a sure way to damage the pipe. The use of commercial heat tapes isn't encouraged because the units usually lack sufficient thermostatic controls necessary to prevent pipe damage. Portable hair dryers and blow combs can be employed, but not entirely without risk. A good rule of thumb is to constantly test the pipe surface with your fingers to assure that it is merely warmed, rather than heated.

Drain Waste Vent & Hot-Cold Water **Vinyl Plumbing** PLUMB-IT-YOURSELF

it's easy with *Genova*

MEET GENOVA

Back in the mid-sixties, a hardware dealer introduced me to Genova's CPVC (chlorinated polyvinyl chloride) miracle hot and cold water supply piping system. The strong, rigid pipe could be cut with an ordinary handsaw, joined to its fittings by easy solvent welding. I tried it and liked it.

Later, in 1968, I featured CPVC in my first home plumbing how-to book. In researching for that book, I became acquainted with a rather unique fellow, R. F. Williams, then president, now chairman of the board, of Genova, Inc. Williams' background as a licensed master plumber, as well as an expert in the field of plastics, made him eminently qualified to assist me in dis-spelling the mysteries of plumbing. Williams' goal was to make home plumbing something that a homeowner could easily do himself. Williams went about it by providing the pipes and varied fittings necessary for the plumbing projects most home handyman plumbers need.

Since then, whole lines of Genova pipes and fittings have been developed by the senior Williams and his son, R. M. Williams, current Genova president and also a licensed master plumber.

The firm's goal has been reached. Vinyl plumbing is not only easy to install, but vinyl lasts longer and works better than other piping systems.

The firm's motto is: "Genova, the people who get it done."

Having worked closely with R. M. Williams in this book's preparation I've seen, firsthand, how diligently that motto is pursued. So, it's no mere happenstance that the name Genova and do-it-yourself plumbing are quickly becoming synonymous.

For us do-it-yourself home plumbers, as well as for the pro's, Genova is the way to go in home plumbing.

R. F. Williams
Michigan Master Plumber, License #04287

R. M. Williams
Michigan Master Plumber, License #05275

ABOUT THE AUTHOR

The author, like Genova, has been a pioneer in promoting successful and easy do-it-yourself methods for home plumbing. He was first to call the homeowner's attention to CPVC pipe and fittings some ten years ago. His three previous books on home plumbing all have brought the latest information on water supply piping with vinyl. This, his fourth plumbing book, brings you the whole story on Genova vinyls.

A do-it-yourself writer in the home and workshop field for nearly a quarter of a century, Day has written numerous articles and books on home repairs and improvements. During the course of that, he built two houses from the ground up, doing every task from bricklaying and concrete masonry to electrical and plumbing work.

Author Day lives in California with his wife, Lois, and their three children. His hobbies range from tending the 120-acre wilderness ranch on which he resides to automotive tinkering and private flying. He is an officer in the National Association of Home and Workshop Writers, which he helped to create.

Richard Day's clear, informative writing style makes a superb introduction to the world of easy-do vinyl plumbing.

Richard Day

EDITOR: Laurie Alberts

PRODUCTION
MANAGER: Jim McIntosh

TYPESETTER: Wendy Gates

PHOTOGRAPHS: Richard Day

WRITER: Richard Day